RUNNING
FOR WOMEN

RUNNING FOR WOMEN

A Basic Guide for the New Runner

MANFRED STEFFNY & ROSEMARIE BREUER

Foreword by Jacqueline Hansen

A Runner's World Book

**Collier Books
Macmillan Publishing Company
New York**

**Collier Macmillan Publishers
London**

Macmillan Publishing Company
866 Third Ave., New York, NY 10022
Collier Macmillan Canada, Inc.

Library of Congress Cataloging in Publication Data

Steffny, Manfred, 1941-
     Running for women.

     "Runner's World Books."
     1. Running for women. I. Breuer, Rosemarie.
II. Title.
GV 1061.18.W66S74 1985   796.4'26   85-3738
ISBN 0-02-029640-1

Macmillan books are available at special discounts for bulk purchases for sales promotions, premiums, fund-raising, or educational use. For details, contact:

Special Sales Director
Macmillan Publishing Company
866 Third Avenue
New York, NY 10022

10 9 8 7 6 5 4 3 2 1

Printed in the United States of America

CONTENTS

Manfred Steffny — Chapters 1,2,3,4,7,14,15,16
Rosemarie Breuer — Chapters 6,9,10,11,12

FOREWORD

Eight o'clock, Sunday morning, August 5, 1984, marked an historic moment in athletics, as 50 women from 29 countries toed the line for the first-ever women's Olympic marathon. The moment had not come easily. It took years, indeed decades, of efforts by runners, coaches, lobbyists, and sportsmedicine practitioners alike to convince governing officials that women distance runners both desired and deserved parity with their male counterparts in the Olympic Games. Women's participation in the Games has never been taken for granted. On the contrary, from the inception of the Olympics, women have had to force their way in, against a great deal of institutionalized resistance.

Pierre de Coubertin, founder of the International Olympic Committee, made his position clear in a 1912 speech: "We feel that the Olympic Games must be reserved for men . . . We feel that we have tried and that we must continue to try to achieve the following definition—the solemn and periodic exaltation of male athleticism with internationalism as a base, loyalty as a means, art for its setting, and female applause as reward."

In spite of that prevailing attitude, Frenchwoman Alice Milliat, founder of the Women's International Sports Federation, succeeded in staging an independent Women's Olympics in the 1920s, with hundreds of international track and field athletes participating in eleven events—including the 1000 meters, which was longer than any event for women in the IOC Games until 1972.

In response, the International Amateur Athletics Federation, fearful of losing control over the growing feminine faction of the sport, co-opted the women's organization in 1924 by promising to recommend inclusion of women's events in the Olympics. After four years of debate over "suitable" events, an abbreviated slate of five women's track and field events (the men had 22) were introduced at the 1928 Games in Amsterdam.

For certain Olympic officials, the most significant women's event at Amsterdam was the 800 meters, the longest distance for the "ladies." Six of the nine finalists collapsed in exhaustion at the finish. Never mind that all six had bettered the existing world record. The United States Olympic Committee report of the 1928 Games noted that "the sport governing bodies of America have not encouraged competitions for women in the half-mile or similar distances" and were not going to do so in the future. The IAAF adopted the U.S. position and the 800 meters was dropped from subsequent Olympic Games until 1960. It took 32 years to reinstate the 800 meters, and another 12 years to add the 1500 meters (or half a century to equal the number of events available in the Women's Olympics of 1922). And yet another 12 years passed before the inclusion of the 3000 meters and the marathon for women.

One longtime advocate of women's distance running who had never accepted the persisting myth of "female frailty" was Dr. Ernst van Aaken. Early on, he had seen through the ill-founded and perverse interpretation of the infamous Amsterdam 800 meters. Between 1953 and 1959, in his hometown of Waldniel, West Germany, he trained such successful middle-distance runners as Marianne Weiss, Margaret Bach, Josefine Bongartz, and Anni Erdkamp. These women regularly competed at 800 meters and in longer cross country events—without collapsing. Van Aaken had said, "What woman has not yet attained, she definitely will attain one day as the result of training methods specifically suited to her."

In 1969, van Aaken seized the opportunity to prove his point, and to showcase women's capabilities as distance runners before a doubting media. In response to the skeptical publicity surrounding fifteen-year-old Canadian Maureen

Wilton's "astonishing" 3:15 marathon—then the fastest ever by a woman—van Aaken staged a demonstration marathon race with his own women runners. The result was a new "world best" of 3:07 set by Anni Pede-Erdkamp. In 1973, van Aaken personally sponsored the first of a series of international women's marathons in Waldniel. These races forever dissipated the myth of women's inability to race long distances and paved the way for the subsequent worldwide boom in female participation that a decade later would at last gain Olympic cachet.

During the same era, van Aaken also coached men—including Olympians Harald Norpoth and Manfred Steffny. Steffny, who competed in Olympic marathons at Mexico and Montreal, has gone on to become one of Europe's foremost running journalists and a successful coach, especially of women distance runners. He is editor of *Spiridon* (the *Runner's World* of West Germany), and his best-known runner, Christa Vahlensieck, twice set a world-best in the marathon.

I first met Manfred and Christa at van Aaken's home prior to the 1974 Women's International Marathon in Waldniel. Since that time, our paths have crossed many times. On New Year's Eve 1975, Christa and I finished first and second, respectively, in the first female division of the famed Sao Silvestre Race in Sao Paulo, Brazil. At the New York City Marathon in 1978, it was Manfred who told me Christa (then the world-record holder) considered a first-time Norwegian entrant, Grete Waitz, the favorite—not only to win but to break the world record (both of which Waitz did).

Though Christa was unable to finish that New York Marathon, she still competes successfully, in her mid-thirties, and continues to set personal-best times. As for Manfred—besides his continuing accomplishments as a coach, writer and runner—he has been an activist on behalf of women distance runners. In 1979, he readily accepted a place on the International Runners Committee, and continues to lobby for Olympic parity for women.

Van Aaken, unfortunately, did not live long enough to see women run a marathon in the Olympics. Better than most, Manfred knows how instrumental his mentor was in seeking its inclusion, and realizes, too, the number of people van Aaken touched with his philosophy, "Run slowly, run daily, drink moderately, and don't eat like a pig."

Jacqueline Hansen, twice the world-record holder in the women's marathon, is the executive director of the International Runners Committee, a lobbying group for athletes' rights.

INTRODUCTION

Are women different from men? As runners, the answer certainly is yes. And since they are different, women require a book that addresses their specific running needs. Certainly, they deserve more than a cursory chapter in some book devoted to running in general.

The late Ernst van Aaken was an early, eloquent and untiring proponent of women's running. As both a runner and coach, I had the good fortune to profit from Dr. van Aaken's wealth of knowledge. In the late 1960s I applied his training methods to a number of talented German women, at distances ranging from 1500 meters to the marathon. This was a heady, exciting time, for we were pioneers in the field. Fifteen years ago, conventional sporting wisdom considered women running any distance beyond 100 meters as taboo.

Dr. van Aaken believed that women are physically and psychologically better suited than men for distance running, and some recent statistics are starting to bear him out. The upswing in the number of women running in the United States has been encouraging. According to Dr. John Pagliano, a well-known podiatrist in Southern California, "The ratio of patients we are seeing now is about 70 percent male and 30 percent female. Ten years ago it was almost all male, say nine to one."

According to a 1983 study by Mediamark Research Incorporated for *Runner's World* magazine, there are 12 million runners in the United States, and nearly five million of them are women.

It is hoped that this book will help move those figures closer to an even balance. We want to help beginning women

runners get more out of their sport, and encourage sedentary women to begin a fitness program. So this book will ignore the training schedules of elite marathoners and concentrate on the needs of beginners. While the first step cannot
help but be the most difficult, we hope to make it easier.

Conditions for women's running remain far from ideal,
just as women's emancipation is not yet universal. Unfortunately, this holds true for more progressive nations as well as
those infamous for the oppression of women. For example,
Andrea Auknitzer of Austria, the former holder of her nation's record for the 25-kilometer run, says, "Fellow athletes
from Germany often congratulate me on winning races the
Austrians know nothing about. As the only woman competing, I am often not mentioned in any of the newspaper stories or race results. There are no official Austrian best times
for distances over 25 kilometers and there are no championships conducted in the marathon."

Similar conditions existed in West Germany and the
United States as recently as 10 years ago. Even today, virtually every newspaper and magazine blares the name of the
men's winner in headlines, while the race's fastest woman is
lucky to get mentioned in the small type. "Until recently, it
has only been the self-assured woman who has dared to
run," says West German runner Ute Daas. "The weaker, less
independent women have stood on the sidelines and
watched."

According to van Aaken, the situation is unnatural as well
as unfair. "While a man runs explosively, and at times errati-
cally, the woman runs steadily, with greater endurance, and
with greater tolerance for pain. In theory, it appears that
women marathoners are more likely than men to run the second half of a race as fast or faster than the first half."

Dr. Joan Ullyot, an American marathoner, sports physician
and author, says, "Women run more realistically than men,
they overestimate themselves less often, and don't hold such
high expectations; hence, they run more consistently with
proportionally more success."

Compared to men runners, women have less body weight,
less muscle (23 percent of body weight compared to 40 per-

cent for men), less water and more calcium in the cells, more adrenal hormones, a more favorable ratio of heart volume and oxygen uptake to body weight, more iron-binding protein in the form of transferrin or siderophilin, more total protein and ionized calcium, a liver with a more efficient metabolism, a greater regenerative power and ability to recover from injury and illness, more active fat, and a pelvic structure better suited for walking or running long distances.

The late Dr. Ernst van Aaken sits among fellow supporters of the women's running movement. Far right, Kathrine Switzer.

An imposing list! What this means practically, and whether the best female runners can ever exceed their male counterparts, will be addressed in a later chapter.

Only a tiny percentage of women runners will ever compete in the Olympics; however, the enhanced self-esteem coming with a transformed body, along with the sheer joy of the act of running, are far more important than winning medals for most women.

"I could no longer conceive of a life without running," is a common refrain in letters from women runners. "Running has become part of my daily routine," writes Jessica Lucas of San Francisco, "and I feel very badly if I miss too much."

The first female marathoners were virtually sisters-in-arms. Even today, this attitude lingers. Men commonly run by each other without exchanging glances. Women assume a different perspective.

"When I meet someone for the first time, and learn that they run, I automatically feel like there is a bond," says Carol L. Irvine of Upper Marlboro, Maryland. "Other runners, for example, are very unlikely to smoke, so I'll not have to worry about that. Runners are more likely to be healthy, stable and independent. These characteristics are an indication that any potential friendship will be comfortable and sound. And it's important to be the kind of friend you want to have."

Enhanced self-confidence is a benefit commonly noted by many runners. "It seems that women aren't as vocally competitive as men, but they still get many similar benefits—a feeling of strength, health and peace," says Irvine. "Women runners I talk to are sounding like they are gaining in self-confidence, that here is something they can do as well as men—maybe not in terms of speed, but in terms of getting fit. When I run in women's races, I feel like my competitors are my sisters, and that we're all working together to help one another."

We would like to express our heartfelt thanks to all the women who contributed to this book. Special thanks goes to Mrs. Koch and Mrs. Hartman of the National Institute for Sports Science in Cologne, West Germany, for their help in avoiding bureaucratic tangles and smoothing the acquisition of literature.

—*Manfred Steffny*
Hilden, West Germany

—*Rosemarie Breuer*
Cologne, West Germany

ONE:
THE DISTINCT
RUNNING STYLE
OF THE WOMAN

The educated eye is able to distinguish between a male and female runner at a great distance, simply because of the difference in strides. Muscle interaction varies in the two sexes. Put simply, a man runs in a muscular, linear fashion, while a woman's running is usually more fluid and circular.

However, the beginning woman runner's stride is typically less efficient than a man's. The athletically inclined man runs powerfully, at times appearing to be lurching and stumbling along the ground. In a group of female beginners, on the other hand, you often see a wide variety of postures and mannerisms. These can be caused by several factors—ill-fitting shoes, tight clothing and—more serious—inhibitions about exercising in front of other people.

Any comparison between male and female runners must begin with the feet. Our society encourages boys to use their feet, while girls are often subtly and blatantly guided to a more sedentary way of life. "Every boy kicks tin cans around in the street," says Professor Manfred Steinbach, "and girls don't."

While women's athletics have enjoyed a renaissance during the last decade, it hasn't altered the basic fact that a woman's foot is not only smaller than a man's, but narrower and weaker as well. Women's running shoes are adjusted to compensate for this difference. Normally, shoe models are constructed on a man's last, or mold, but scaled down. So a woman's size six is shaped like a man's size six, but cut shorter.

The dexterity of the female foot is at least equal to that of the man's. For proof, you need look only as far as the toe work of a prima ballerina. Women also often exceed men in manual dexterity. A recent survey showed that women were six percent faster performing manual work than a comparable group of men. When I think about the wine harvest on the Moselle River in West Germany and the speed at which the women fill their buckets with grapes, I consider the six percent figure to be low.

Tight, high-heeled shoes are often to blame for women having such a difficult time starting to run. Years of forcing feet into insufficient spaces can lead to a splayed or pointed foot. A pointed foot typically results in a light, skipping stride that shouldn't be mistaken for proper running form. At the very least, a woman should exchange her fashionable footwear for flat heelless shoes on a day when she plans to run.

Tight, high-heeled shoes also cause a shortening of the Achilles tendon, making it susceptible to injury when placed under a heavy strain or load. But the Achilles will stretch and grow stronger once flat shoes are worn for a period of time. When beginning female runners complain of Achilles tendon problems, it is often not the tendon itself that is painful, but the attached calf muscle, the soleus. This painful condition can usually be alleviated within two or three days by applying hot compresses or soaking the ankle in hot water.

Another common foot problem resulting from ill-fitting shoes is hallux valgus, a condition in which the big toe bends inward and eventually develops bunions. In severe cases the big toe is actually bent underneath the other toes. Running can help correct hallux valgus, but only if the patient is careful to buy shoes with an extra-roomy toe box.

PROPER RUNNING STYLE

There are two fundamental styles of running: toe-heel and heel-toe. The toe-heel style, commonly employed in sprinting and middle-distance running, entails landing on the ball of the foot. The stride is of average length, and makes great demands on the calf muscles.

Distance running most often employs the heel-toe method, in which the runner lands on his heel and utilizes the muscles in the hip and pelvic region. This latter style is more difficult to learn for those men who possess weak lower back muscles. Women, on the other hand, readily learn the heel-toe method, provided they haven't spent too much time wearing high heels. High heels promote running on the balls of the feet.

In principle, both styles are equally fast. One is not inherently better than the other. It is important to remember that running is not merely a function of the foot. In the proper running motion, the arms, knees, hips and lower back are all called into play. Think of the action of a pair of scissors. While the blades do the cutting, the power is generated from the handle. At times you'll see people trying to run without lifting their knees, and you'll remember that running is not as natural as it seems. Many people must relearn how to run!

A woman concerned about her appearance should realize that different running styles can have varying effects on the figure. The toe-heel style tends to accentuate the calf muscles. The heel-toe style, on the other hand, will slim down the calves, since the strain on these muscles is eased by the extensive use of the hips and pelvic area.

The broad pelvic girdle of women inclines them toward straddle-legged running. Women, therefore, should try to run with their legs as close together as possible, especially on flat turf or pavement. The foot should plant on the sole's outer edge and then push off from the ground using a greater surface area of the shoe's sole. In an overextended stride, the body's center of gravity is misplaced. Besides appearing stiff and clumsy, an overextended stride is also inefficient and slow. Wider placement of the feet can relieve or prevent minor injuries or soreness.

When running, it is important to place equal stress on both feet. Easing the pressure on one foot will overburden the

Grete Waitz, Norway's great marathoner, displays excellent running form.

other. Unequal distribution of work normally results in injuries to the stronger, lead foot.

Another pitfall to avoid is pronation, or the excessive inward roll of the foot. If the running shoe's outer sole wears faster on the medial side than the lateral side (the opposite is normally the case), it is a strong indicator of pronation. The runner who pronates, twists and strains the tibia, causing irritation that can lead to chronic inflammation. The only cure for pronation is prevention, which is accomplished by selecting the right type of running shoe and amending your stride to eliminate the excessive inward roll.

Due to her pelvic structure and low center of gravity, the woman athlete is less likely than a man to excel in sprinting and middle-distance running. Physique, however, does not work against female long-distance runners.

Weak lower-back muscles lead to slackening and misalignment of the upper torso. Instead of striding smoothly, the runner kicks back into space and leans farther and farther forward as she tires. One of the best ways to correct this problem is to practice watching a spot eight to ten yards in front of you as you run. Also, improved posture while walking and sitting will help strengthen the lower back, as will specific calisthentics and stretching exercises.

Large-breasted women face a special problem. Their physiques promote running with rounded or hunched shoulders. In a proper running style the shoulders are held back, the muscles around the collarbone are stretched taut, the arms are held parallel to the body—acting as pendulums for the leg motion—and the hands are held with partially open palms. The forearms shouldn't be held too high, and the shoulders shouldn't be hunched. If your elbows are moving directly above your hips, chances are you're running with the proper body lean. Also, be sure to run with the legs close together and the arms close to the torso. Some people stride so inefficiently that a soccer ball could be pushed between their arms and upper body.

Many men run with clenched fists, causing them to cramp up, and the resulting tension spreads all the way through

Gayle Barron maintains correct running style while racing in the Avon Marathon.

their bodies. Women, happily, are likely to run with far less tension. The pounding style of running often observed in beginning male runners is seldom found in women. Likewise, a man's paunch is more bothersome on a run than the extra padding on a woman's buttocks and thighs.

To summarize: A woman's stride is shorter than a man's due to her smaller foot and degree of leverage. The forward thrust of her hips and the functioning of her pelvis puts the woman in better distance-running stride or gait than the man. She favors the heel-toe style of running, which is superior for covering longer distances. The woman's larger breast is supported while running by increased action of the hips and torso; the man, meanwhile, must work his arms more vigorously.

"A man's movement has a more pounding, active character, while a woman's is more rolling and passive," Dr. Stratz stated a century ago. "While a man seeks to achieve fleeting balance, the woman strives to maintain the existing form."

Every human movement is a continuum, an interchange between lengthening and contraction of the muscles. In women, the lengthening element is more pronounced, while in men the dynamic, contracting element is stronger. It is a great mistake to prescribe a male's running style to a woman, merely because it is faster. If nothing else, the flowing style of a woman has one distinct advantage: It is gentler and leaves the woman less susceptible to injury.

TWO:
THE HISTORY OF WOMEN'S LONG DISTANCE RUNNING

It was horribly crowded on the bed of the beer truck, where a few benches had been set up for reporters and photographers. The truck started slowly, and all the passengers aboard grabbed hold for a windy ride. Behind us, 262 women from twenty-four countries were preparing to run the Avon Marathon in Waldniel, West Germany. The date was September 22, 1979, and the race would serve as the unofficial marathon world championship for women.

"Isn't it beautiful to see all these women at the start?" shouted Kathrine Switzer, the American organizer of the race. As the starting gun fired, the runners' collective scream drowned out the cheers of the spectators, and Switzer herself let out a yell from the truck. It was as if she were back at the 1967 Boston Marathon, running in the otherwise all-male field. Eventually a race official caught on and tried to physically remove her from the competition. The photograph of Switzer's running partner putting a cross-body block on official Jock Semple was transmitted throughout the world. Ironically, that photo was the start of a long but ultimately successful struggle of the marathon's "emancipation" movement.

"Manfred," Switzer said, nudging me. "I think we did it!" Moved by the historic event, my eyes became misty.

Britain's Joyce Smith would win this groundbreaking marathon for women, in Dr. Ernst van Aaken's hometown, with a time of 2:36:27. Thirty-six women finished in under three hours. The race's message was loud and clear: Women were in the marathon to stay.

By "it, " Switzer was referring to a variety of things, among them the inclusion of a women's marathon in the Olympics. The previous winter, Switzer had been invited to London to address a meeting of the International Amateur Athletic Foundation, and impressed the mostly elderly, ill-conditioned men with her lecture and slide show arguing for a woman's marathon at the Los Angeles Olympics in 1984. At the same time, the International Runner's Committee had engaged the International Olympic Committee in a similar lobbying effort. An important ally was found in IOC director Monique Berlioux of Switzerland. In February 1981, the good news was released: In Los Angeles in 1984, women would be vying for gold, silver and bronze medals in the 26.2-mile run.

Unfortunately, the triumph came too late to be witnessed by Melpomene. In 1896, Melpomene, a young Greek woman, wanted to participate in the marathon at the first modern Olympics in Athens. Her request was denied on two counts: First, in support of the male-only policy of the original Games, women were barred from competing in any event. Second, of all the events, Melpomene wanted to run in the most demanding. According to legend, a Greek messenger died of exhaustion at the Athens gates after delivering the news of victory over the Persians at Marathon.

Melpomene, however, had little patience for tradition or legend. Accompanied by two cyclists, she ran the Olympic marathon course a few days before the race, finishing in a respectable 4:41 (Spiridon Louis, also of Greece, won the gold medal in 2:58:50).

It wasn't until 1928 that women's track and field events were included in the Olympics. Baron Pierre de Coubertin, the founder of the modern Games, was unsympathetic toward female athletes. Upon hearing that women would be included in the Amsterdam Games, de Coubertin retired from public life.

Yet it was at those 1928 Olympics that women's running suffered a severe setback. Untrained sprinters began the 800-meter run at much too fast a pace. German Lina Radtke-Botschauer won in a world-record time of 2:16.8. Yet the eyes of the world were drawn to the back of the pack, where most of the runners had collapsed before the finish line. An uproar spread over the debacle at this "unwomanly distance." Shortly thereafter, the women's 800 meters was removed from the Olympic program, not to reappear until the 1960

Jock Semple unsuccessfully tries to eject Kathrine Switzer from the Boston Marathon.

Games in Rome. For 32 years, women were only allowed to sprint in the world's most important athletic competition. Olympic organizers had committed an error with serious implications.

As it turns out, women are inferior to men in terms of muscle composition and explosive strength required for sprinting. The longer the distance, however, the more a woman can utilize her natural endurance and hardiness. But 800 meters is a distance particularly ill-suited to women, because their ability to withstand the severe oxygen debt is decreased. "When I think how, earlier, we always ran the wrong distance, and how sometimes we blacked out after 600-meter runs, I still get angry today," says Sylvia Schenk.

The West German 800-meter champion in 1972, Schenk today is a district court judge in Frankfurt, a leader in the women's sports movement, and she still runs for her health.

Before World War II, one of the few groups promoting women's long-distance running was the Tarahumara Indians of Mexico. According to legend, a Tarahumara chief responded to an invitation from a Kansas marathon by sending three women from the tribe (the Tarahumara run up to 100 miles a day). Another voice in the wilderness belonged to Violet Piercey, who ran the 1926 Polytechnic Marathon in 3:40.

Beginning in 1947, Dr. Ernst van Aaken championed the cause of women's distance running. From his base in the Rhine Olympic Sports Club, van Aaken helped show just how capable women runners could be.

In 1954, the women's 800 meters made a comeback at the European championships, and six years later was reintroduced at the Olympics. In 1969 a similar pattern emerged with the 1500 meters. That year the event was included in the European Championships, and in 1972 the women's metric mile became part of the Munich Olympics.

Proponents of women's running hoped that a similar fate would await the 3000 meters after it was included in the European Championships in Rome in 1974, when Finland's Nina Holmen won the race in 8:55.4. Two years later, however, the IOC removed the women's 3000 meters from its list of proposed Olympic events. After years of slow but steady progress, women's running had suffered a demoralizing setback.

Meanwhile, on the roads, other women were fighting for the right to run. In 1966, Roberta Gibb ran the Boston Marathon—perhaps the world's best-known non-Olympic marathon—without a starting number and was ignored by race officials. Kathrine Switzer, then 20 years old, prepared carefully for the 1967 Boston Marathon and registered under the name "K.V. Switzer." Race official Jock Semple's attempt to remove her from the race had the ironic effect of transforming Switzer into a running heroine. She became one of the best known female athletes in America. Her attempt was

Joan Benoit celebrates after her historic 2:22:43 world record in the Boston Marathon.

more a pioneering effort than a great sports performance, but it was an effort noted around the world. Switzer devoted herself to the cause of women's athletics, and six years later Boston organizers officially welcomed women into the race. In 1973 Switzer acted as a race official, and in the prerace press conference the famous "reconciliation kiss" took place between her and Semple. Although Switzer would never fulfill her dream of officially winning the women's portion of the Boston Marathon, she would eventually improve her time to a fine 2:51 clocking. In her present role as public relations consultant with Avon, Switzer organizes a full calendar of women-only races, with the Avon Marathon serving as the unofficial world championship for women.

When news of American women's marathons reached West Germany, Dr. van Aaken responded, "We can do that in Waldniel." In 1967, his protégée, Ann Pede, won the Waldniel Marathon in a world-best 3:07:27. In 1971, American Beth Bonner broke the three-hour barrier with a time of 2:55:22.

Virtually year by year, the record has been broken. Among the memorable record-setting performances were West German Liana Winter's 2:42:24 at the 1975 Boston Marathon. The same year Christa Vahlensieck lowered the record to 2:40:15, and in 1977 she bumped it down to 2:34:47.

1978 ushered in the Grete Waitz era. Starting that year, the Norwegian progressively lowered the world record in the New York City Marathon, dropping the time to 2:25:41 in 1980. In April 1983 American Joan Benoit won the Boston Marathon in 2:22:43, the present world-best time. A year later Benoit won the gold medal in Los Angeles in 2:24. Records will surely continue to fall like leaves on a windy autumn day.

With quality also came quantity. In 1984, among the 100,000 marathoners in the United States, 15,000 were women. In central Europe the number of women marathoners is between 5 and 10 percent of the total number of participants, a figure that is increasing steadily.

MIDDLE- AND LONG-DISTANCE RUNNING OF WOMEN AND THEIR INTERNATIONAL RECOGNITION

1928: Introduction of the 800 meters as an Olympic event (as the only running event besides the 100 meters and the 4×100 relay, in addition to the high jump, discus throw).
Olympic champion 800 meters: Lina Radke-Batschauer (Germany)—2:16.8

1932: Cancellation of the 800 meters from the Olympic Games (with the addition of the 80-meter hurdles and the javelin throw).

1954: Introduction of the 800 meters into the European Championships.
European champion 800 meters: Nina Otkalenko (Soviet Union)—2:08.8

1958: Introduction of the 400 meters into the European Championships.
European champion: Maria Itkina (Soviet Union)—53.7

1960: Reintroduction of the 800 meters into the Olympic Games.
Olympic champion: Ludmilla Schezowa (Soviet Union)—2:04.3

1964: Introduction of the 400 meters into the Olympic Games.
Olympic champion: Betty Cuthbert (Australia)—52.0

1969: Introduction of the 1500 meters into the European Championships.
European champion: Jelena Jehlickova (Czechoslovakia)—4:10.7

1972: Introduction of the 1500 meters into the Olympic Games.
Olympic champion: Ludmilla Bragina (Soviet Union)—4:01.4

1974: Introduction of the 3000 meters into the European Championships.
European champion: Nina Holmen (Finland)—8:55.2

1980: Introduction of the 3000 meters World Championships.
World champion: Birgit Friedmann (West Germany)— 8:48.05

1983: Introduction of the Marathon World Championships.
World champion: Grete Waitz—2:28:09

1984: Introduction of the Olympic Games marathon.
Olympic champion: Joan Benoit (United States)—2:24:52

THREE:
WOMEN UNDER
SCRUTINY—WHAT
CAN
THEY ACHIEVE?

Almost all assessments of runners' capabilities are based on performances by men. Most authorities have recommended taking a man's performance and adding 10 to 20 percent to arrive at a comparable women's time. For example, to receive a marathon badge from the German Track and Field Association, a man must run the distance in four hours, and a woman in four and a half hours. The times required for men and women to win sports certificates in other long-distance races, however, have been totally disproportionate. A man younger than thirty-two must run 5000 meters in twenty-three minutes, a time many athletic but untrained men cannot achieve. On the other hand, a twelve-minute mark for 2000 meters for women younger than twenty-eight is much easier to achieve than the men's 5000-meter requirement. Other age-group standards are also lower for women than men. Here are the men's running standards for German sports badges:

5000 METERS

18-31	under 40	under 45	under 50	under 55	under 60	over 60
23 min.	25 min.	28 min.	31 min.	34 min.	36 min.	38 min.

And now the sports badge standards for women:

2000 METERS

18-27	under 35	under 40	under 45	under 50	under 55	over 55
12:00	12:40	13:20	14:00	15:00	16:00	17:00

5-K (Walk)

18-27	under 35	under 40	under 45	under 50	under 55	over 55
—	50 min.	52:30	55:00	55:00	55:00	55:00

A similar situation exists in the junior ranks. For girls, age thirteen and fourteen, to achieve bronze badges in the 1000 meters, they need only run the distance in six minutes; girls fifteen and sixteen must run it in five minutes. The standard for girls seventeen and eighteen in the 1500-meter run is nine minutes. These minimal standards reflect the outdated yet still existent thinking about the endurance of women distance runners. However, the standards are appreciably higher for certificates in other endurance sports. For example, for a woman age eighteen to twenty-seven, a respectable time for a 10-kilometer cross-country ski race is set at 54 minutes. A time of one hour earns a certificate for a 20-kilometer bike ride, while twenty-nine minutes is the standard for the 1000-meter swim.

To arrive at realistic values for rating women's long-distance running performances, one can look at the results of major women's road races. The biggest and most significant run for women is the Bonne Bell 10-K, a run in June in New York City's Central Park. The race is run over a relatively flat course, and the field is large and varied: in 1981, 4137 women finished. The nature of the event is less competitive than cooperative, a celebration of sisters-in-arms. As a result, the Bonne Bell serves as a revealing cross section of women's running. In the 1981 race:

Mini-Marathon: 10-K, New York, 1981

11 under 35 minutes	79 between 35 and 40 minutes
90 under 40 minutes	169 between 40 and 45 minutes
259 under 45 minutes	424 between 45 and 50 minutes
683 under 50 minutes	660 between 50 and 55 minutes
1343 under 55 minutes	811 between 55 and 60 minutes
2154 under 60 minutes	794 between 60 and 65 minutes
2948 under 65 minutes	544 between 65 and 70 minutes
3492 under 70 minutes	317 between 70 and 75 minutes
3809 under 75 minutes	165 between 75 and 80 minutes
3974 under 80 minutes	93 between 80 and 85 minutes
4067 under 85 minutes	38 between 85 and 90 minutes
4105 under 90 minutes	

The last of the 4137 finishers was an eight-year-old girl who clocked in at 1:51.

If you plot a graph of these results, using minutes and the number of runners as coordinates, you'll see a steeply rising parabola with a solid, wide middle around one hour. Approximately 10 percent of the runners finished in less than forty-eight minutes, which qualifies as a "good" rating, and about half were under one hour, a figure that a hard-working woman of average athletic ability can attain after one year of running. Running a 10-K in one hour or less, then, would be considered "satisfactory."

Clearly, a set of times calculated strictly for women is overdue. The following numbers are valid for a test run after at least one year of running.

1. Very good   = 10-K under 40 minutes
2. Good   = 10-K between 40 and 48 minutes
3. Satisfactory   = 10-K between 48 and 60 minutes
4. Sufficient   = 10-K between 60 and 75 minutes
5. Inadequate   = 10-K between 75 and 90 minutes
6. Unsatisfactory   = 10-K over 90 minutes

This evaluation is valid for women between the ages of fifteen and forty-five. Outside this range an "age bonus" would be necessary.

Such an age bonus exists in Dr. Kenneth Cooper's aerobic test, which entails running 1.5 miles. While this distance might be optimum for testing beginning athletes, better-trained athletes should turn to longer distances. Trying to run a relatively short distance faster and faster will not bring you into top condition. The goal should be to run as long a distance as possible without rest.

AEROBIC STANDARDS FOR WOMEN
ACCORDING TO COOPER: 1.5 MILES

Category	Under 30 years	30-39 years	40-49 years	Over 50 years
Very good	Under 11 min.	Under 11:30	Under 12:30	Under 13:30
Good	11:01-13:30	11:31-14:30	12:31-15:30	13:31-16:30
Satisfactory	13:31-15:30	14:31-16:30	15:31-17:30	16:31-18:30
Inadequate	15:31-17:30	16:31-18:30	17:31-18:30	18:31-20:30
Poor	Over 17:30	Over 18:30	Over 18:30	Over 20:30

The Road Runners Club of America has produced a standard subdivision made up of twelve distances. The lowest level, Class C, would still correspond to a "good" rating in our standards for 10-K runs. For this reason, our evaluation is of interest only to competitive female athletes or coaches. Again, what's most interesting are the varying standards of evaluation.

WOMEN'S STANDARDS, ROAD RUNNERS CLUB OF AMERICA

	World Class	Master	Class A	Class B	Class C
10-K	33:00	35:30	38:00	41:30	45:30
15-K	52:30	56:00	1:00:30	1:06:00	1:12:00
20-K	1:11:00	1:16:00	1:22:00	1:29:00	1:37:30
25-K	1:29:30	1:36:30	1:44:00	1:53:00	2:04:00
30-K	1:49:00	1:57:00	2:06:30	2:18:00	2:31:00
Marathon	2:38:00	2:50:00	3:04:00	3:20:00	3:39:30
50-K	3:10:30	3:25:00	3:41:30	4:01:30	4:25:30

A provocative question is whether women could equal or surpass men's performances in the marathon or 100-kilometer run. Dr. Wolfgang Klemm, a gynecologist and marathoner from Leipzig, East Germany, responds, "Women trained for long distances are highly resilient. They appear particularly well-suited for very long distances, based on their smaller and lighter constitution and their level of metabolism, which leads to a more efficient utilization of fatty acids. In the psychological domain, women are equal to men in the areas of tenacity, preparation and will power, and are able, at least in part, to give more of themselves. In the circulatory and respiratory systems, however, a woman's physical disadvantages are manifest. The woman's circulatory and respiratory systems operate approximately 8 to 12 percent less efficiently than a man's."

Examining these questions brings up one of the most controversial questions in sportsmedicine: Where is the limiting factor for endurance-running located? Is it centrally located in the circulatory and respiratory systems, or is it in the periphery—in the metabolism of the muscles? Recent arguments have been put forth viewing the heart and lungs as the controlling organs of long-distance running. I share

this view. Contained in this theory is the answer to the earlier question of whether the best female runners could outrun comparably trained males in the marathon or 100-kilometer run. Based on research currently available, the answer seems to be no. Women's advantages in fat metabolism cannot offset their more severe disadvantages in the uptake and transportation of oxygen. Thus, when comparing men's and women's world records, a differential extends through all the running events. This differential of 8 to 12 percent appears in the longer distances also, including the marathon. In the 100-K, the difference is even greater.

Besides her disadvantages in the heart and lungs, a woman's biological fluctuations can also have a detrimental effect on her level of competitiveness. Even women with a slender body type and a natural talent for running have great difficulty finishing a marathon under 2:30.

Given these facts, however, women should hardly be discouraged about distance running. For the opportunity to compete is probably the least of running's many advantages. By running, a woman can control her weight and enhance her self image; she can stay in tune with her family, her environment, her career and herself. Compared to these benefits, running fast seems relatively insignificant.

FOUR:
THE TRAINING
OF THE FEMALE
RUNNER

A woman's distance-running training is virtually the same as a man's. A woman generally goes into oxygen debt relatively quickly, and thus cannot tolerate a hard, fast pace as well as a man. Her circulatory system, though, can adapt as well as a man's. This means that her long-distance training program can be identical. Due to her limited oxygen uptake capacity, however, she should be more careful when running uphill; in spite of an equivalent strain on the pulse, she will become short of breath more quickly than a man.

But even with beginners, it is a positive sign that a woman recovers relatively quickly from the exertion of a long run. The scene repeats itself after almost every marathon: Women almost always recover more quickly than men in the first ranks of finishers.

Later we will discuss the reasons for a woman's quick recovery, which include a favorable strength-load ratio, larger reserves of subcutaneous fatty tissue and a more favorable hormone metabolism.

Although women do display a remarkable level of innate hardiness and endurance, they are not immune from the ravages of modern life. While a man's heart is often directly affected by sedentary living, resulting in a heart attack or severe angina, a woman is more likely to experience symptoms in the peripheral circulatory system. Specifically, she might suffer irregularities in her blood pressure. Whether the blood pressure is too high or too low, any irregularity is unpleasant for beginning women runners. Hypertonics (people with high blood pressure) commonly run with a flushed face, while hypotonics (those with low blood pressure) might become as white as a sheet. High blood pressure is often related to excessive weight, but is also linked to an individual's genetic predisposition. A sensible long-distance running program can be one of the best remedies available for treating high blood pressure.

Unfortunately, oral medication remains the medical establishment's standard treatment for hypertension. Doctors and patients should closely monitor the gradual buildup in dosage. High blood pressure (except in extreme cases) subsides more quickly through running than taking medication. Often, patients who run can stop taking medication much earlier than originally recommended.

In general, low blood pressure is a less serious condition. Regular long-distance running helps regulate blood pressure, and after a period of training blood pressure levels often return to normal. A beginning woman runner with lower than normal blood pressure might experience tired legs during a workout. This is particularly likely to occur during the walking phase of a workout, when the blood pressure drops rather rapidly. Yet the woman who perseveres through this stage will be amazed at how stable her blood pressure will become. She will learn that she doesn't need three cups of strong coffee to get going in the morning, that it is more beneficial and natural to jog 200 steps on her bedside rug each morning.

In 1977, I designed a one-year running program for the German Sports Association. By the end of the year, the four groups in the program were to reach the following goals:

Group I: One hour of long, slow distance-running in a single session.

Group II: One hour of distance running in a single session at a faster pace.

Group III: Ten kilometers in fifty minutes.

Group IV: A half-marathon (13.1 miles) in two hours.

I will explain the first three months of training for the four groups. This phase is commonly known as the training base.

The training is divided into three sessions per week, a frequency that has proven to provide the most favorable degree of cardio-respiratory stimulation. Running just once a week places insufficient stress on the body. After six days of inactivity, you regress to your original level of fitness. The absolute minimum is two distance runs per week. A better level of fitness is obtained through three half-hour sessions of endurance sports per week. Other basic requirements include:

• Reaching at least 50 percent of your maximum running speed.

• Keeping your pulse rate at 120 to 140 beats per minute during a workout.

• Never running at a speed at which you can't hold a normal conversation. Being able to run and talk comfortably at the same time is the litmus test of an anaerobic workout. In anaerobic speedwork, a runner is continuously short of breath.

Professor Wildor Hollman of the German Sports College in Cologne proposes ten-minutes of endurance training daily. It has been shown, however, that it is both more practical and efficient to consolidate the training into three weekly sessions of longer duration.

PROPER DIVISION OF GROUPS

It is not recommended for the out-of-shape beginner who has led a sedentary life to run more than three times per week for the first year of training. The body must gradually grow accustomed to the new demands being placed upon it. The beginning runner who attempts daily training is likely to suffer some painful setbacks, ranging from sudden, inexplicable loss of proper running form to frequent injury. A woman cannot be inactive for years and then abruptly start exercising without inviting injuries. It is much more enjoyable and productive to start gradually and gently. When the organs, muscles and tendons have adjusted, the training can be increased. A woman wishing to add a fourth training day can do so, provided it takes the form of a low-key long run.

At the start of the program, the groups are divided according to their base levels of fitness:

Group I: The totally untrained, overweight or convalescent.

Group II: The healthy but under-trained; women who can tolerate fifteen minutes of running at a slow pace.

Group III: Those who can run at a slow pace for thirty minutes without stopping.

Group IV: Women who already are experienced runners or athletes from other sports who can run for an hour at a time.

These categories look very neat on paper, but in practice it is often difficult to place a woman in the correct group. Certainly, most older women will immediately gravitate toward Group I, but where do we place a female hockey goalie? Is she Group III, Group IV or perhaps only Group II? Where do we place a cheerleader or bowler?

The best proven testing method is the Harvard Step Test, which has been administered to thousands of patients in the United States. The test was developed at Harvard University in cooperation with the American Medical Association. The four-minute test provides reliable information on the patient's circulatory fitness. An alternative method would be to use a stationary bicycle, but I have yet to find a reliable bicycle ergometer test. In a five-minute ergometer test an athletic but out-of-shape woman can compensate for organic weakness with leg strength. But the Harvard Step Test is similar to climbing stairs: The subject must continually overcome the force of gravity. In addition, the steps become proportionately higher with taller subjects. The test requires blocks of wood that bear the following correspondences to height:

5 feet = 11.7 inches
5 feet to 5-foot-3 = 13.6 inches
5 3½ to 5-9 = 15.6 inches
5-foot-10 to 6 feet = 17.5 inches
6 feet and taller = 19.5 inches

The block of wood should have a surface area large enough to be stepped on with the entire foot. A chair or coffee table might work in place of a block of wood. A stair step is typically about seven inches high. So if you climb two steps (fourteen inches) and your height is five-foot-four, the test results should be accurate.

The subject climbs on and off the block of wood for four minutes, performing thirty repetitions for a total of 120 steps. You can keep time by one of two methods: Use a metronome, or find a partner with a stopwatch. The effort should certainly cause you to break into a sweat.

After four minutes, sit down and take your pulse. The first pulse measurement should be taken between five and five and one-half minutes. The second should follow between six and six and one-half minutes, and the third between seven and seven and one-half minutes. Then add these three readings together to arrive at the pulse sum:

$$\text{recovery index} = \frac{\text{length of exercise time (in seconds)} \times 100}{\text{pulse sum} \times 2}$$

If you cannot last the entire four minutes and must step off the block after two to three minutes, you cannot calculate an accurate recovery index. Most often, the test subject will become wobbly in the knees before the stress on the circulatory system becomes too great. This is an example of the body's protective mechanism, which also functions during a run. Before the heart is unable to handle the strain placed upon it, the peripheral musculature—namely, the legs—will give out.

The following mean values were reached for the Harvard Step Test (the results are applicable to the general population):

Recovery index

under 60	poor
61-70	satisfactory
71-80	good
81-90	very good
over 90	excellent

Accomplished marathon runners commonly score 120 or higher. The Harvard Step Test is particularly valuable because it can be repeated to provide a reliable measurement of the subject's improved fitness. On the other hand, it can reveal the presence of a hidden infection or other illness if there is a sudden, unexplained drop in the index.

In my opinion, the Harvard Step Test is vastly superior to the 1.5-mile Cooper test. The Cooper test encourages a fast, hard run over a relatively short distance and neglects long-distance runs, which are more effective barometers of aerobic fitness.

The chief disadvantage of the Harvard test is that some people cannot accurately measure their own pulse. Yet the Harvard Step Test, with its wood block, metronome and watch, remains the simplest, cheapest and most convenient fitness measuring device. We must not allow ourselves to be seduced by hi-tech paraphernalia!

Once your recovery index is determined, you can be placed in one of the four groups:

Under 50 = Group 1; 50-60 = Group 2; 61-70 = Group 3; 71-80 = Group 4.

If you score higher than 80, the training program proposed here will be too easy for you. Congratulations! I can recommend my book *Marathoning* for further reading. But you might be able to learn how to add supplemental elements to your training regimen by studying this program. The text is like a cookbook—you needn't try every recipe. Pick and choose the workouts that seem best suited for your fitness goals.

During the year-long program, different training methods are utilized. Their application is useful both for women following the total program and for those who are tailoring an individual program.

This plan offers several advantages. It is based on distances that have already been successfully completed rather than future times to be met, which distinguishes it from other plans. For example, a half-mile is a daunting distance to a beginning runner, and is likely to cause a great deal of distress if it appears suddenly on a training schedule. On the other

hand, beginners tend to underestimate an "eight-minute run," beginning too quickly and running into a demoralizing oxygen debt.

It is only slightly more complicated to measure distances in forests, fields and parks than to calculate from mile markers or maps. It is easier to stick to a standard distance than to guess how far you're running.

At the German College of Physical Education in Leipzig, East Germany, untrained adults were trained for one year. Three groups trained either one, two or three times a week. The improvement in fitness was determined by means of a test run of 1.24 miles. The results supported the opinions of most trainers as if they were ripped verbatim out of a textbook. After three months all of the runners reached evaluation level one for the 1.24-mile run (this translates to a sub-7:30 for people age eighteen to twenty-nine, a sub-8:15 for age thirty to thirty-nine, a sub-8:45 for age forty to forty-nine and under ten minutes for age fifty to fifty-nine).

The women ran slightly more than one mile instead of 1.24 miles, receiving a bonus of 15 percent. The group that trained twice weekly required twice the amount of time—six months—to achieve the same performance levels as the runners who trained three times a week. People training only once a week required nine months to reach a comparable level. All participants improved an average of 23.6 percent over the entire year.

A second Leipzig test was also very interesting; unfortunately, it involved only male subjects. Runners accustomed to training two or three times a week were allowed to train only once a week for an entire year. This reduction resulted in a remarkable drop in fitness level, with an average of thirty-four running minutes per week. Only those subjects who ran as long as forty-five minutes were able to maintain their levels of fitness. It is generally thought that rest periods of ten to fourteen days between individual workouts eliminates all progress. The physical conditioning deteriorates such that the athlete has to begin training all over again.

One inspiring example is German runner Carin Fischer. Although moderation is always advised, and each individual proceeds at her own pace, Fischer provides a model of what can be achieved. She made a name for herself by becoming the first German to conquer the Swedish Endurance Classic (186 miles of bicycling, 18.6 miles of running, 1.9 miles of swimming in a river and 37.2 miles of cross-country skiing) with an intense yet minimal amount of preparation. After seventeen days of running, she entered a sixty-two-mile run, but dropped out at fifty miles. A week later she finished the Karwendel Run (thirty-three miles with a 1.2-mile elevation increase) in seven hours and forty minutes.

RUNNING TRAINING: GROUP I

Week 1

This program is designed for slow increases but steady progress. The three days per week of exertion (ideally one day of training followed by one day of rest) will train the muscles and cardio-respiratory system equally. The daily schedule should not be altered or skipped, for each step is dependent upon the previous one. For many women, modest, continuous stimuli rather than sudden, strenuous efforts will best train the body for competition and endurance. The person who wants to become a long-distance runner must be patient.

Training Day 1:
Ten minutes of interval running; jog about 50 yards, walk a 50-yard pause, 50-yard jog, 50-yard walk, and so on.
Training Day 2:
Repeat Day 1.
Training Day 3:
Ten minutes of interval running, in which the jogging intervals can be increased to 100 yards, and the walking pause remains at 50 yards.

Week 2

Severely overweight, beginning runners and con-valescents should occasionally take their pulse after the running or jogging section during the walking pause. The pulse, ideally, should never be more than 140 beats per minute. If the pulse is more than 150, the requirements for long-distance running are no longer met (equal stress upon both the lungs and heart). If the pulse climbs higher, the pace must be slowed by a comparable amount. In a few cases, the pulse remains higher during the first few weeks and drops gradually as the body adapts. In any case, pulse values nearing 180 indicate your heart is working at absolute maximum. Only experienced athletes in good health should stress themselves to this extent.

Training Day 1:
Five-minute warmup
Ten × 100-yard jog, each with a 100-yard walking pause
Training Day 2:
Five-minute warmup
Ten × 100-yard jog, each with a 100-yard walking pause
Training Day 3:
Five-minute warmup
Five × 150-yard jog with 50-yard walking pauses

Week 3

An evenly paced long-distance run is the training goal. The beginner must prepare for it by running shorter intervals; otherwise the muscles will become overtaxed after a few minutes. The intervals should always be completed as an integrated whole, in which the last run should still be run at the same pace as the first one, if possible. This holds true for the length of the walking pauses as well.

Training Day 1:
Five-minute warmup
Five × 150-yard jog with 50-yard walking pauses
Training Day 2:
Five-minute warmup
Five × 200-yard jog, each with 200-yard walking pause
Training Day 3:
Five-minute warmup
Five × 200-yard jog, each with 200-yard walking pause

Week 4

The warmup plays an important role in training. Muscles and organs are prepared for the increased demands on the body. Almost as important is the warmdown. During this period the muscles become revitalized, and breathing and circulation make a smooth transition toward a normal workload. Until now, the warmdown has been missing from the training program, because it would mean an additional workout for the beginner. From now on, it becomes a regular part of the program.

Training Day 1:
Five-minute warmup
Six × 300-yard jog (untimed), each with 100-yard walking pause
Five-minute warmdown
Training Day 2:
Five-minute warmup
Eight-10 × 200-yard jog, each with 100-yard walking pause
Five-minute warmdown
Training Day 3:
Five-minute warmup
Six × 300-yard jog, each with 100-yard walking pause
Five-minute warmdown

Week 5

Gradually, the clock comes into play. The approximate interval times are given in order to prepare the runner for an increased pace later on. For many athletes the clock is a restraining factor, because they run too quickly. The individual sections should be run in oxygen-equilibrium. That is, the pace should be so slow that you still have extra oxygen available, for example, to talk with a partner during the run.

Training Day 1:
Five-minute warmup
Six × 300-yard jog in approximately 2¹/₂ to 3 minutes, each with 100-yard walking pause
Five-minute warmdown

Training Day 2:
Five-minute warmup
Ten × 200-yard jog, each with 200-yard walking pause
Five-minute warmdown
Training Day 3:
Five-minute warmup
Six × 300-yard jog in approximately $2^{1}/_{2}$ to 3 minutes, each with 100-yard walking pause
Five-minute warmdown

Week 6

You may be one of a large number of runners for whom the training build-up does not progress quickly enough, and who wants to reach the competitive level as quickly as possible. You should be patient. You must allow your body time to adapt and avoid possible setbacks from forced training. The woman for whom the increasing program already presents difficulties shouldn't give up. She can repeat the initial sessions as often as necessary, until she can master the next step in the program. This holds especially for heart patients.

Training Day 1:
Five-minute warmup
Ten × 300-yard jog, each with 100-yard walking pause
Five-minute warmdown
Training Day 2:
Five-minute warmup
Five × 300-yard jog, each with 100-yard walking pause
Additional five-minute walking pause
Continuous half-mile run
Five-minute warmdown
Training Day 3:
Five-minute warmup
Ten × 300-yard jog, each with 100-yard walking pause
Additional 2 × 600-yard jog
Five-minute warmdown

Week 7

After six weeks of preparation the overall well-being of most runners has increased and they've enjoyed noticeable weight loss. The long-distance running can now begin. For the first time you can anticipate the long-distance run as a pleasurable "horseless ride," without being restricted by muscular and breathing difficulties. But the maxim continues to hold: slow, but steady!

Training Day 1:
Five-minute walk and run
Additional five-minute run in one direction and return
Five-minute warmdown
Training Day 2:
Ten-minute interval running (approximately 100-yard jog and 50-yard walk)
Training Day 3:
Five-minute walk and run
Additional five-minute continuous run in one direction and return
Five-minute warmdown

Week 8

The pulse should be taken occasionally during the long distance run: For this purpose, a break of only ten to fifteen seconds should suffice. Measure the pulse for ten seconds immediately after stopping by placing the tip of the thumb against the carotid artery directly under the jaw bone. The pulse is easier to find there than on the wrists. If the pulse is too high, run slower.

Training Day 1:
Fifteen-minute continuous run, with walking pauses in case of shortness of breath or other difficulties
Training Day 2:
Five-minute warmup
One × 300-yard jog in approximately 2^1/$_2$ minutes, each with 100-yard walking pause
Five-minute warmdown
Training Day 3:
Five-minute continuous run in one direction and return

Week 9

A particularly effective variation of the long-distance run is a cross-country jaunt in one direction. After a predetermined time, turn around and retrace your route. Proper cadence and pace will allow the runner to run to and from the turning point in the same length of time. A prerequisite is a country road with little change in elevation. Most runners start too fast and have a difficult time maintaining pace during the second half of the run.

Training Day 1:
Five-minute warmup
Ten-minute run with a turnaround point
Five-minute warmdown
Training Day 2:
Five-minute warmup
Ten × 300-yard jog in approximately $2^{1}/_{2}$ minutes, each with 100-meter walking pause
Five-minute warmdown
Training Day 3:
Fifteen-minute continuous run with walking pauses in case of shortness of breath or other difficulties

Week 10

On many training days an earlier session will be repeated. The logic behind this repetition is that you can compare your present fitness level with previous efforts. Expect improvements to appear within eight days.

Training Day 1:
Five-minute warmup
Ten × 300-yards in approximately $2^{1}/_{2}$ to 3 minutes, each with 100-yard walking pauses
Five-minute warmdown
Training Day 2:
Five-minute warmup
Fifteen-minute continuous run with walking pauses in case of shortness of breath or other difficulties
Five-minute warmdown

Training Day 3:
Five-minute warmup
Three × 600-yards in approximately five to six minutes,
each with three- to four-minute walking pauses
Five-minute warmdown

Week 11

The long distance run, which gradually forms more of the training base, must not be one-dimensional. With the runs including timed turnaround points, you can closely monitor your increased distance and fitness.

Training Day 1:
Ten-minute interval running (jogging and walking)
Additional 3 × 800-yard jog in eight to ten minutes
Five-minute pause between each repetition
Five-minute warmdown
Training Day 2:
Five-minute warmup
Fifteen minutes of continuous running
Five-minute warmdown
Training Day 3:
Five-minute warmup
Ten × 300 yards in approximately 2½ to three minutes

Week 12

By the 12th week an important portion of the buildup has been completed. At the end of this week the runner should complete a test run, ideally on the track, of a distance between 2000 and 3000 yards. A target time is not given; you should, however, record your time for future reference. If you can lengthen the test run to 3000 meters, and achieve a time of between 20 and 22 minutes, you may skip one step in the training.

RUNNING TRAINING GROUP II

Week 1

Training Day 1:

Easy five-minute warmup (jogging and walking). Six × 300-yard run (pace should be adjusted so that it can be held through the last run) at approximately three minutes per run.

One hundred-yard walking pauses between the runs.

Training Day 2:

Five-minute warmup (see above)

Six × 300-yard jogs, each in about three minutes with 100-yard walking pauses; five-minute warmdown

Training Day 3:

Five-minute warmup

Six × 300-yard jog in three minutes, each with 100-yard walking pauses

Five-minute warmdown

Week 2

The 300-yard intervals are the segments which prepare the runner for the upcoming long-distance runs. The program should be seen as a unified whole, in which the transition phases are fluid. Later, an entire long distance run will be undertaken at this pace. You should be used to running with an even rhythm by now.

Training Day 1:

Five-minute warmup

Eight × 300-yards in approximately three minutes; five-minute warmdown

Training Day 2:

Twenty-minute interval running (100-yard jog, 100-yard walk, 100-yard jog, and so on.)

Training Day 3:

Five-minute warmup

Eight × 300 yards in approximately three minutes

Five-minute warmdown

Week 3

The slow, long distance run is introduced here. The pace should not be exhausting, nor should it cause excessive sweating. It should be run at a speed at which you can hold a conversation. The long runs can be broken up with walking pauses, if necessary.

Training Day 1:
Twenty-minute run with one-minute walking pause after 10 minutes
Five-minute warmdown
Training Day 2:
Five-minute warmup
Ten × 300-yards in approximately $2^{1}/_{2}$ minutes
Five-minute warmdown
Training Day 3:
Twenty-minute long-distance run with one-minute walking pause after 10 minutes
Three-minute warmdown

Week 4

A run in the country serves as good endurance training. After running to a predetermined turning point, return along the same route. Good cadence and pace will help you run to and from the turning point in the same length of time. A prerequisite is a country road with little change in elevation. Most runners start too fast, and have a difficult time maintaining their pace during the second half of the run.

Training Day 1:
Ten-minute run in one direction and return
Training Day 2:
Five-minute warmup
Five × 600-yards in approximately five to six minutes, each with a $1^{1}/_{2}$-minute walking pause
Five-minute warmdown
Training Day 3:
Ten-minute run in one direction and return
Five-minute warmdown

Week 5

Training Day 1:
Five-minute warmup
Six × 300-yards in approximately 2^1/$_2$ minutes, each with a one-minute walking pause
Five-minute warmdown
Additional ten-minute pause and an easy ten-minute run

Training Day 2:
Five-minute warmup
Twenty-minute run with a one-minute walking pause
Five-minute warmdown

Training Day 3:
10-minute warm-up
Two × 800-yards in approximately 18 minutes, both with a three-minute walking pause
Five-minute warmdown

Week 6

In the build-up phase there is a parallel increase in endurance, with a goal of running as long as possible at one time while gradually increasing your pace. Six weeks of physical build-up are the minimum. Therefore, a 2000-meter test run is scheduled for the end of the sixth week, ideally completed on measured, flat terrain or a track.

Training Day 1:
Ten-minute run in one direction and return

Training Day 2:
Thirty-minute run with a walking pause after approximately 10 minutes

Training Day 3:
Ten-minute warmup
Two thousand-yard test run in approximately 16 minutes
Five-minute warmdown

Week 7

An easy week, with neither timed intervals nor strenuous distance runs
Training Day 1:
Five-minute warmup
Relaxed, 10-minute run
Five-minute warmdown
Training Day 2:
Thirty-minute interval run (100 yard jog, 100-yard walk)
Training Day 3:
Thirty-minute run with a turn-around point
One-minute rest at the turn

Week 8

The running intervals lengthen—600-yard runs are now on the program. They should be run in five minutes. Now one can speak of tempo runs, in which the runner should wear the lightest running gear possible, taking into account the weather. A flat path in the woods or on the track will make the task easier, while the countryside will suffice for the long-distance runs.
Training Day 1:
Five-minute warmup
Three × 600-yards in approximately five minutes, each with a two-to-three-minute walking pause
Training Day 2:
Twenty-five-minute run with a one-minute walking pause, if necessary
Training Day 3:
Thirty-minute interval run—200 yard jog, 100-yard walk, 200-yard jog, and so on

Week 9

The warmup is necessary before tempo or interval running, in order to prepare the body for the ensuing exertion. As you become more experienced, you might be able to skip these warmups before the runs. Instead, begin the workout more slowly and increase the pace; after a few minutes settle into your proper rhythm. Allow your legs and breathing to become more relaxed. The warmdown also becomes superfluous when you can finish a continuous run at a gentle pace.

Training Day 1:
Thirty-minute run with a turn-around point
Training Day 2:
Ten-minute warmup
Two × 1000-yards in seven minutes, each with a three-minute walking pause
Ten-minute warmdown
Training Day 3:
Thirty-minute run in the countryside or on a circular path

Week 10

Sprint training appears on the program for the first time. You shouldn't fly out of the starting blocks like a track sprinter, but run as loosely and comfortably as possible. Sprinting will develop new muscles; therefore, expect stiff legs. If you are over 50, be careful with the sprints!

Training Day 1:
10-minute warmup
Five × 100-yard relaxed sprint
Ten-minute run
Five-minute warmdown
Training Day 2:
Thirty-minute run with conscious deep-breathing
Training Day 3:
Thirty-minute run with turnaround point

Week 11

The long distance runs have been enjoyable when done without time checks. This week more must be done to build stamina, so that a quicker pace can be maintained over a specific period of time. Increased running skill, however, makes possible a workload that could only be dreamed about a few weeks ago.

Training Day 1:
Ten-minute warmup
Three × 1000-yards in seven minutes, each with a
three-minute pause
Training Day 2:
Twenty-five-minute warmup
Ten × 300-yards in 2 to 2¹/₂ minutes, each with a
one-minute walking pause
Five-minute warmdown
Training Day 3:
Thirty-minute run, with walking pauses when necessary

Week 12

The twelfth week ends an important section of the
build-up. A two-mile test run should be attempted at the end
of the week, with a goal of finishing in approximately twenty
to twenty-two minutes. Flat, open country or a running track
will suffice, or a quiet country road (remember to run facing
traffic).
Training Day 1:
Thirty-minute run
Additional 5 × 100-yard relaxed sprints
Five-minute warmdown
Training Day 2:
Easy 30-minute run
Training Day 3:
Ten-minute warmup
Three thousand-yard test run, ideally run on a track in 20
to 25 minutes

RUNNING TRAINING GROUP III

Week 1

This long distance running program is designed to increase slowly and progress steadily. The three days per week of exertion (ideally one day of training followed by one day of rest) should train the different muscles equally. Ideally, the daily schedule shouldn't be altered or skipped, for each session builds upon the previous one. For some, the demand is insufficient; yet modest, continuous stimuli, rather than sudden, strenuous efforts will best prepare the body for competition and endurance. The person who wants to be a long-distance runner must be patient.

Training Day 1:
Easy five-minute warmup (jogging and walking). Six × 300-yard run, with the pace calculated so that it can be held through the last run (under no circumstances faster than two minutes per run), with 100-yard walking pauses between the runs.

Training Day 2:
Five-minute warmup
Six × 300-yard run with 100-yard walking pauses
Five minutes of slow warmdown

Training Day 3:
Five-minute warmup
Six × 300-yard run in 2 to $2^{1}/_{2}$ minutes with 100-yard walking pauses; five-minute warmdown

Week 2

The slow, long distance run is added as a new element. The pace shouldn't be exhausting, nor should it cause excessive sweating. Run slowly enough to be able to comfortably hold a conversation. Complete the 300-meter runs at a steady pace. The interval runs and pauses should be viewed as a unified whole.

Training Day 1:
Five-minute warmup
Eight × 300-yards in approximately 2 to 2¹/₂ minutes, each with a 100-yard walking pause
Five-minute warmdown
Training Day 2:
Twenty-minute run with a two-minute walking pause every five minutes
Training Day 3:
Five-minute warmup
Eight × 300-yards in approximately 2 to 2¹/₂ minutes, each with a 100-yard walking pause
Five-minute warmdown

Week 3

Training Day 1:
Thirty-minute run with a one-minute pause every 10 minutes
Five-minute warmdown
Training Day 2:
Five-minute warmup
Ten × 300-yards in approximately 2 to 2¹/₂ minutes
Training Day 3:
Thirty-minute run with a one-minute pause every ten minutes

Week 4

A run in the country is an excellent training tool. Run to a predetermined turning point, and return. Good cadence and pace will allow you to go out and back in the same length of time. A prerequisite, though, is a country road with little change in elevation. Most runners start too fast, and have a difficult time maintaining their pace during the second half of the run.
Training Day 1:
Ten-minute run in one direction and return
Training Day 2:
Five-minute warmup
Five × 600-yards in approximately 4 to 4¹/₂ minutes

One to 1½ minute pause after each interval
Five-minute warmdown
Training Day 3:
Ten-minute run in one direction and return
Five-minute warmdown

Week 5

The balance of oxygen consumption and intake ("the ability to speak while running") is one of the restrictions placed on long distance runs; the pulse rate is the other. During the run the pulse should not exceed 140 beats per minute. It is best to measure the pulse during the run or shortly thereafter. Ten seconds immediately after the run will suffice. The pulse is best measured by placing the tip of the thumb on the carotid artery, directly under the jaw bone. The pulse is found more quickly there than on the wrist. If the pulse exceeds 150, run more slowly.

Training Day 1:
Six × 300-yards in 2 to 2½ minutes with one-minute pauses between runs
Additional three-minute pause
Two × 600-yards (untimed)
Training Day 2:
Ten-minute warmup; easy, 20-minute run with one-minute pauses if necessary; five-minute warmdown
Training Day 3:
Ten-minute warmup
Two 1000-yard runs in 6 to 7 minutes
Three-minute pause
Five-minute warmdown

Week 6

In addition to building stamina—running as far as possible without pauses—the pace is gradually quickened. The faster the pace, the longer the stride must be. At the outset, you achieve a longer stride by deliberately lifting the knees while running. The arms should be carried parallel to the legs. The previous six weeks formed the first portion of your long distance training. At the end of the sixth week there is a

3000-meter test run, ideally conducted on the track or on a flat, measured country road.

Training Day 1:
Thirty-minute run (include short jogging pauses, if necessary)
Training Day 2:
Ten-minute warmup
Five × 300-yards in 2 to 2$^1/_2$ minutes
Ten-minute warmdown
Training Day 3:
Three thousand-yard test run without a time limit (try for twenty to twenty-two minutes

Week 7

You've earned an easier week after the test run. After two days of long-distance running, sprint training appears on the program for the first time. You shouldn't make a contest out of this, but run as relaxed as possible. During the sprints you will inevitably develop new (hence, stiff) muscles, as in the beginning of training.

Training Day 1:
Five-minute warmup
Easy 15-minute run
Training Day 2:
Thirty-minute run with turnaround point
Training Day 3:
Ten-minute warmup
Five × 100-yard relaxed sprints, each with a one-minute pause
Five-minute warmdown

Week 8

The distance runs are gradually lengthened. The tempo runs require a flat, easy route in a forest or park, or a visit to the track. The tempo runs should be completed in the lightest clothes possible, taking the weather into account.

Training Day 1:
Five-minute warmup
Five × 600-yards in four minutes with 2 to 2^1/$_2$-minute pauses
Five-minute warmdown
Training Day 2:
Forty-minute run; with one-minute walking pauses every 15 minutes if necessary
Training Day 3:
Ten-minute warmup
Five × 100-yard relaxed sprints
Ten-minute pause
Thousand yards in five to seven minutes
Five-minute warmdown

Week 9

The warmup before the tempo runs are necessary in order to prepare the body for the ensuing exertion. You can skip them before distance runs. Begin slowly and increase the pace after a few minutes. Find the right rhythm, and make sure to keep the legs and breathing relaxed. The warmdown becomes unnecessary when you can finish the long distance run comfortably.

Training Day 1:
Forty-minute run with turnaround point
Training Day 2:
Three × 1000-yard in six minutes, each with a three-minute pause
Ten-minute warmdown
Training Day 3:
Forty-minute run in the open country or on a circuit route

Week 10

If you're growing bored with your long-distance runs, look for a training partner or change your routes. Changes offer comparison with earlier training efforts, in addition to prettier countryside. The timed runs with turnaround points should continue to lengthen. Short circuit runs also accurately reveal your current fitness level.

Training Day 1:
Forty-minute run interrupted by five relaxed, fifty-yard sprints
Walking pauses after the sprints, if necessary
Training Day 2:
Thirty minutes of gentle running with conscious deep-breathing
Training Day 3:
Forty-five minute run
Walking pauses, if necessary

Week 11

Repetitions in the training program occur so that you can monitor the progress in your form and fitness. Instead of running 5×1000 yards, try going 2×2000 yards or 4×1200 yards.

Training Day 1:
Ten-minute warmup
Five $\times$ 1000 yards in $5^1/_2$ to 6 minutes
Pause every three minutes
Five-minute warmdown
Training Day 2:
Five-minute warmup
Ten $\times$ 300-yards in two minutes; five-minute warmdown
Training Day 3:
Forty-minute run; walking pauses when needed

Week 12

An important part of the build-up ends with the twelfth week. At the end of the week, try to complete a 5000-meter test run in 30 minutes. Those who run slower than 30 minutes might attempt the program for Group 2 instead of Group 3. The others have completed their test.

Training Day 1:

30-minute run

Additional 5×100-meters at a relaxed pace

Training Day 2:

Forty-minute run with walking pauses if necessary

Training Day 3:

Ten-minute warmup; 5000-yard test run (ideally on the track)

Try for 30 minutes or faster

Ten-minute warmdown

RUNNING TRAINING GROUP IV

Week 1

This running program is designed to increase slowly and progress steadily. The three days per week of exertion (ideally one day of training followed by one day of rest) should train the different muscles equally. Ideally, the daily schedule should not be altered or skipped, for each step builds upon the previous one. For some the demands might seem insufficient; yet modest, continuous stimuli, rather than sudden, strenuous efforts will best train the body for endurance. The person who wants to be a long distance runner must be patient.

Training Day 1:
Easy, five-minute warmup
Six × 300-yard run; the pace should be slow enough so that it can be held through the last run; under no circumstances should it be faster than two minutes per run
One hundred yard walking pauses between the runs

Training Day 2:
Five-minute warmup
Eight × 300-yard run, each with 100-yard walking pauses
Five-minute warmdown

Training Day 3:
Five-minute warmup
Eight × 300-yard runs at approximately 2 to$^1/_2$ minutes with 100-yard walking pauses
Five-minute warmdown

Week 2

The slow, long distance run is added as a new element. The pace shouldn't be exhausting, nor should it cause excessive sweating. Run slowly enough to be able to comfortably hold a conversation. Complete the 300-meter runs at a steady pace. The interval runs and pauses should be viewed as a unified whole.

Training Day 1:
Five-minute warmup
Thirty-minute run with a one-minute walking pause every 10 minutes

Training Day 2:
Five-minute warmup
Ten × 300-yards with 100-yard walking pauses
Five-minute warmdown

Training Day 3:
Thirty-minute run with a one-minute walking pause every 10 minutes

Week 3

A run in the country makes an excellent training tool. Run to a predetermined point and return. Good cadence and pace will allow you to run to and from the turning point in the same length of time. A prerequisite is a country road with little change in elevation. Most runners start too fast and have a difficult time maintaining their pace during the second half of the run.

Training Day 1:
Five-minute warmup
Ten-minute run in the open country in one direction and return
Five-minute warmdown

Training Day 2:
Five-minute warmup
Five × 600-yard run in approximately 4 to $1/2$ minutes, each with a 1 to $1^1/2$ minute pause
Five-minute warmdown

Training Day 3:
Ten-minute run in one direction and return

Week 4

The balancing of oxygen consumption and intake ("the ability to speak while running") is one of the restrictions of long-distance runs; the pulse rate is the other. During the run, the pulse should not exceed 140 beats per minute. It is best to measure the pulse during or shortly after the run. Ten seconds immediately after the run will suffice. The pulse is best measured by placing the tip of the thumb on the carotid artery directly under the jaw bone. The pulse is found there more quickly than on the wrist. If the pulse exceeds 150, run slower.

Training Day 1:
Five-minute warmup
Twenty-minute run with turnaround point

Training Day 2:
Four × 600-yard run in approximately four minutes, each with a one-minute pause; three minutes rest, then run second series of 4×600-yards in four minutes, each with a one-minute pause; five-minute warmdown

Week 5

In addition to building stamina—to run as far as possible without pausing—the pace is gradually quickened. The faster the pace, the longer the stride must be. At the outset, you can achieve a longer stride by lifting the knees. The arms should be carried parallel to the legs. In tempo running, it is important not to start too quickly. Ideally, you should feel strongest on the final run.

Training Day 1:
Ten-minute warmup
Three × 800-yards in six minutes, each with a three-minute pause
Ten-minute warmdown

Training Day 2:
Thirty-minute run with turnaround point
Five-minute warmdown

Training Day 3:
Ten-minute warmup
Three × 800-yards in six minutes, each with a
three-minute pause
Ten-minute warmdown

Week 6

Six weeks of physical build-up is the minimum for
building stamina. Gradually, the staying power increases,
making difficulties incurred initially less noticeable. Now
you can also think about running faster. For that reason, a
300-yard test run is conducted at the end of the sixth week,
which ideally should be completed on a track or on a flat,
measured, country road.

Training Day 1:
Ten-minute warmup
Ten × 300-yards in two minutes, each with a one-minute
pause
The final 300 yards can be run faster
Twenty-minute warmdown
Training Day 2:
Thirty-minute run in the open country.
Training Day 3:
Ten-minute warmup
Three thousand-yard test run (goal: 18 minutes or faster)
Five-minute warmdown

Week 7

You've earned an easier week after the test run. After two
days of distance running, sprint training appears on the
program for the first time. You shouldn't make a contest out
of this training, but run as relaxed as possible. With the
sprints you will be developing new muscles. Hence, stiffness
can hardly be avoided, especially at the onset of training.

Training Day 1:
Ten-minute warmup
Easy 20-minute run
Training Day 2:
Thirty-minute run with turnaround point

Training Day 3:
Fifteen-minute warmup
Five × 100-yard relaxed sprints, each with one-minute pause
Ten-minute warmdown

Week 8

The distance runs are extended to 45 minutes. The tempo runs require a track or a good, flat running route in a forest or park. While one can easily carry out long-distance runs in a heavy warm-up suit, the tempo runs should be completed in the lightest possible clothing.

Training Day 1:
Ten-minute warm-up
Five × 600-yards in four minutes with 2 to^1/$_2$-minute pauses
Five-minute warmdown

Training Day 2:
Forty-minute run with one-minute walking pause for recovery, if necessary

Training Day 3:
Ten-minute warmup
Five × 100-yard relaxed sprints, 10-minute pause
One thousand yards in five to six minutes
Five-minute warmdown

Week 9

The warm-up is necessary before tempo runs, in order for the body to adjust to the ensuing exertion. You can skip it before long-distance runs. Begin slowly and increase the pace after a few minutes. Find the correct rhythm and make sure that the legs and breathing are relaxed. The warmdown can be skipped if you can complete the long-distance run comfortably.

Training Day 1:
Forty-minute run with turnaround point

Training Day 2:
Ten-minute warmup
Three × 800 yards in five minutes, each with a three-minute pause

Training Day 3:
Ten-minute run in the open country or on a circuit route

Week 10

If you're growing bored with your long-distance runs, look for a training partner or change your route. Changes offer comparison with earlier training efforts, in addition to prettier countryside. The runs with turnaround points should be continuously lengthened. Short-circuit routes—in which one can record split-times-accurately reflect your current fitness level.

Training Day 1:
Ten-minute warmup
Five × 1000-yards in five minutes, with a three-minute pause after each
Five-minute warmdown.

Training Day 2:
Forty-five minute run, broken up with five sprints of 50 meters
Include walking pauses, if necessary.

Training Day 3:
Thirty-minute distance run with conscious deep breathing.

Week 11

In a training program that repeats itself, you can readily monitor your progress. Along the way you might notice some mysterious fluctuations that you can't explain. The tempo runs can be varied. Thus, the total effort is the same, whether you run one mile five times, or two miles two times at the same pace.

Training Day 1:
Ten-minute warmup
Five × 800-yards in five minutes, each with a three-minute pause
Five-minute warmdown

Training Day 2:
Five-minute warmup
Ten × 300-yards in $1^1/_2$ minutes
Five-minute warmdown

Training Day 3:
Forty-minute run, ideally without a walking pause, at a steady pace

Week 12

An important part of the buildup ends with week 12. At the end of the week, try to complete a 3-mile test run in 25 minutes.

Training Day 1:
Ten-minute warmup
Three × 800-yards in $4^1/_2$ minutes, pause four- to six minutes
Ten-minute warmdown

Training Day 2:
Easy 40-minute run, with walking pauses if necessary

Training Day 3:
10-minute warmup
Two-mile test run (ideally on the track) Test goal: 23 minutes; 10-minute warmdown.

FIVE:
THE FACTORS
OF FEAR

It has been my observation that women enjoy running more when they do it in groups. I've observed this phenomenon since 1977, when women became more visible on the running scene. The observation extends to major races as well as it does to weekday training runs.

Some would say that it is due to the reputed gregarious nature of women as opposed to men. Others would say that it is something that is learned in society. (Have you observed, for example, how men will excuse themselves from a group to go use the rest room, whereas a woman who finds it necessary to use the rest room invariably shops around for a cohort to accompany her?) Still others might theorize that women band together on training runs and at races out of self-defense against the world in general. This situation also allows them to blend in with an amorphous crowd, thereby downplaying their own physical identity, with which they may not be comfortable, especially if they are somewhat new to this fitness stuff and are still trying to shed a few extra pounds.

Others tend to feel that men—perhaps because of their more extensive sports background in schools—are more prone to compete with each other, and therefore enter even a training run with an unconscious need to physically test their partners. (As with all rules, however, there are exceptions. Certainly there are *very* competitive women runners; I've been on a few furious training runs with them, none of which I initiated. I've also run with groups of men who are all extremely sociable and enjoy just shuffling along.)

Many men become involved in running as their prime fitness activity because of its simplicity. No matter how busy they get during the day, they can usually take out half an hour to get in their training. The needs of the runner are minimal. And for the white-collar worker, running can be done alone and need not wait to mesh with someone else's schedule. Women, however, tend to feel there's strength in numbers, and will often go to great lengths to arrange runs with friends, turning it into more of a social affair. (It is fairly common for a group of women to train together and then to race together in their first 10-K or marathon. Certainly, training together encourages everyone in the group to train at the same speed, which dovetails very nicely toward staying together in a group during the actual race. And there is terrific inbred encouragement and support within the group when the individual members go jointly into new territory, such as a marathon.)

All of these reasons for women training and racing together pale, however, before the most obvious reason: mutual safety.

As a male runner, I've had my run-ins with everything from street gangs to vicious dogs. But it is only through talking with hundreds of women runners over the course of nearly a decade that I can appreciate the deeply felt fear women have of being vulnerable while running.

Many distance runners who train alone have a subconscious fear that someone might be lurking about, waiting for them with intentions of assaulting, mugging or raping them.

Certainly, this fear can be appreciated by men or women who've chanced to walk through a forest path or a dark alley only to come upon a stranger. You tend to feign a walk of authority and perhaps you find yourself whistling away the dark. When you do pass the other person, it is frequently the case that he was as uneasy as you were. Men don't usually transfer those feelings of fear into a daylight situation, but certainly many women do.

When you use this perspective, it is easy to see just how courageous some of the pioneers of the women's running movement were. Many of them, such as West Germany's former marathon record holder, Christa Vahlensieck, did much of their training alone in the mid-1970s.

HARASSMENT ON THE RUN

The female's apprehension about running begins at her front door.

This initial apprehension, of essentially baring yourself to a sometimes cruel world, keeps many women from ever undertaking a running program.

They look at themselves in the mirror, appreciate the fact that they've added a few pounds in places where they aren't flattering and want to do something about it, but don't want to parade themselves in front of the neighbors while they do it. "What are they going to think of me?" she might ask herself. "I really can't do that."

Some women I know refused to go running outside until they looked better in running clothes or until they could come up with a way to camouflage what they looked like as a novice runner. This latter rationale accounts for many of the women runners you see who either run in baggy sweatsuits no matter how hot and humid the day, and also accounts for the preference of many women to run before the sun comes up or after it goes down—both instances increasing the chance of harassment of one kind or another.

Be consoled in the fact that I have known some women, who are quite good runners today, who refused to run outside until they had taken ten or twenty pounds off by running in place indoors or had worked out extensively on a stationary bicycle.

And, to make the process less painful, when you decide on your first run in the outside world, it would be perfectly logical to invite a running friend along to cushion the blow. You'll soon become so comfortable running through the outside world and smelling the roses, that you'll no longer look at it as a chore.

The fears that you may have about running outdoors are often overblown and can often be minimized by taking certain logical steps. Abuse falls into two categories, at least one of which is not confined to women: physical and verbal.

Because men were into distance running long before women, and because they were small in numbers, they were often the subject of verbal abuse—and often the target of empty, and sometimes full, beer bottles. (Thank goodness for today's wide use of aluminum cans!) The male runners who've been at it for a decade or more all have their favorite stories of verbal abuse, and it takes merely the mention of harassment at a cocktail party for them to parade out all their stories.

Because of the increased number of runners in the 1980s (more than twelve million in the U.S. according to a recent *Runner's World* survey), they have become an accepted part of the landscape, and are usually ignored by non-runners unless one happens to cross an intersection against the traffic light.

A lone female runner is a different matter entirely, however. She is often the object of catcalls or lewd remarks or totally unacceptable offers of physical services. Some males who would never think about making a lewd remark to a woman on a bus wouldn't think twice about making an outrageous remark to the same woman if he saw her out running alone. Obscenities are not uncommon to the woman on the run, and often the territory through which you are running determines the nature of the obscenity.

Notice, however, that the same heckler who would not pause to throw a catcall your way when you're alone, skulks off and acts like he's looking the opposite way if you run back in a group or with a particularly fit-looking male. It is no wonder, then, that women tend to gravitate toward group runs: they offer impunity from hecklers while also offering an opportunity for good conversation.

Women runners also tend to be defensive in their dress when they run, often taking great pains to either fade into the scenery or to be as unattractive as they can be. As already mentioned, it is not uncommon to see a woman in a heavy sweatsuit jogging along on the hottest day of summer, instead of in a light tricot singlet that allows her skin to breathe.

It must be admitted that her strategy not only outfoxes hecklers and lechers, but it is also an extra layer of protection against the occasional vicious dog.

Actual physical attacks on women have little to do with their age, how they dress, etc. A rapist is driven by a coarse drive that does not allow him to focus on beauty or attractive clothing. Psychological studies seem to indicate that a rapist is not particular about the object of his attack; a child is just as prone to be raped as a beautiful woman, and an attractive woman is no more likely to be raped than a bag lady sporting rolled down nylon stockings ending in mismatched orthopedic shoes.

Statistically, nearly 50 percent of all rapes are committed within the immediate vicinity of the victim's house. So what good is it if a woman takes precautions to run with a male escort who leaves her at the corner while she's yet to face a thirty-foot walk through a dark entranceway to reach her door?

A woman runner should take certain precautions. Why invite danger?

You should always close and lock windows before you leave your house or apartment, and you should make sure the door is locked behind you when you leave. And don't hide the key under the mat or in the flowerpot next to the door! If you don't want to buy one of the convenient wristband pouches, lace your key through your shoelace and then tie a double knot. Every burglar worth his pry bar knows the typical hiding places for house keys.

If you are going to drive to where you run, lock your car, but don't hide the keys under the bumper or on the tire. Take the key with you; the minor irritation of carrying the key is well worth the precaution.

Also, if you know that it will be dark when you return from a run, turn on the lights before leaving. If you run with a partner, ask him or her to accompany you to the door until you let yourself in safely. If you live alone, it is always a good precaution to merely use your first initial on the mailbox or in the phone book, since that helps avoid attention from would-be criminals. And no matter how impersonal you may feel the world's become, it never hurts to know at least one of your neighbors on a first-name basis.

In *Runner's World* magazine, Michael Pickering, author of *A Women's Self-Defense Manual,* offers the following six recommendations toward minimizing the chance of an attack:

1) Run in brightly lit areas. You can better ward off the danger when you can see in all directions. If you must run through dark areas, quicken your pace.

2) Vary your training route. Never run only one route, where the potential attacker can lie in wait for you. Force yourself, if possible, to continuously run different routes. As a further possibility, you can run your route in the opposite direction. Both possibilities will probably suffice in discouraging a premeditated attack.

3.) Likewise, vary your departure time. The time at which you run should not be predictable. Occasionally begin your training at least fifteen minutes earlier or later.

4) Try to run with a partner. In unity there is strength. If you must run alone, then select a busy time of the day and a busy area of your town.

5) Become well acquainted with your environment. Locate the safe places, so that if attacked, you can easily reach escape routes. You might want to carry a quarter in your running shorts in case you have to make an emergency phone call.

6) Run forcefully. Remain confident. Always be aware of where you run and what you do. The person who is always afraid on the run and constantly looks around is sending off the signals of a potential victim. As a result, an attacker's resolve will only be strengthened. Watch your environment but look confident when you run. Self-confidence is an important quality to exhibit.

Should You Defend Yourself?

A great deal of controversy surrounds the issue of whether a woman should defend herself during an attempted rape. Some experts warn that as a result of such defensive measures, the attacker will only become more aggressive and the danger of bodily harm or even death increases.

On the other side of the argument is the statistic that between 75 and 80 percent of rape attempts that were unsuccessful ended because of the intended victim defended herself. A University of California at Berkeley study contends that some 70 percent of the women who had successfully warded off rape attempts were familiar with self-defense techniques.

Every woman who runs can arm herself with a few workable self-defense techniques. For instance, it is felt that if you are running and you are approached by a rapist, that your immediate best defense is your running itself. By throwing in a burst of speed or a carefully executed side-step, you can often evade the attempt. The rapist is seldom a trained athlete, while you are.

If an attack occurs, the first thing you should do is to begin a controlled scream, even if you have evaded the rapist. It has been proved that shouting the word "Fire!" is much more effective than yelling "Help!" Cries for help are often like crying "Wolf!" and may be misinterpreted, and therefore ignored. (How many girls have you seen running around a park yelling "Help!" at the top of their lungs while roughhousing with a boyfriend?) Also, yelling for help may not work because many people are reluctant to become involved in a physical confrontation. On the other hand, however, a fire attracts people like a magnet. Additionally, yelling "Fire!" has been known to confuse and irritate attackers, occasionally discouraging them entirely.

If you are confronted by an exhibitionist, on the other hand, the best strategy is to ignore him; don't give him the satisfaction of a shocked look. You should immediately report the appearance of an exhibitionist to the nearest policeman. Studies have shown that people who expose themselves are usually harmless and do not physically attack women.

Should your attacker approach from the front, remember that no matter how little you weigh, you have something going for you: your momentum. If an attacker steps out in front of you and prepares to lunge for you, don't slow your pace or he'll capture you; instead, keep running at him. In full stride, you can build up a tremendous amount of force, and even if you aren't trained in a martial art, a single blow from a raised elbow to the guy's head will often work wonders. By doing just that, I was once able to fight off a very surprised pair of chain-swinging hoodlums.

Even if the attacker has stopped you, it is not too late. Michael Pickering has put together a set of ten rules for behavior in such circumstances. It is worth reviewing those rules:

1) Take a step backwards or to the side. Place your hands in front of your upper body as a protective shield.

2) Take special care to protect your upper body and face. Lift your arms high and protect the upper body with one hand and the face with the other. In an attack, the face is the most vulnerable part of your body. If the head is struck severely, serious injuries—and even death—may be the result. The next most vulnerable area is the upper body. Protect the ribs, heart, lungs, etc. The legs, arms and lower body are not vital for survival, so their protection is of secondary importance to the upper body.

3) Block the attacker's arm with one of your own arms, leaving the other arm free to strike back.

4) Immediately kick toward his groin, with the arms positioned as a protective shield. At the same time, step back or to the side. Most attackers do not think of protecting their lower bodies. A well-placed kick can turn a would-be attacker's attention away from you and toward his own problems.

5) Next, attack the upper body while the attacker expects the second kick. Strike out at his head and neck and if he attempts to defend himself, kick at the groin again until you can safely flee.

6) Attack the vital areas of the body, especially when a weapon is drawn. Step aside, out of the weapon's range. If you are still in close, make the eyes your first target when dealing with the upper body. And don't be bashful about gouging with force and with your fingernails; your life is more important than his eyes. If you are grabbed from behind, an elbow in the stomach delivered with some force can

knock the wind out of him long enough for you to make an escape.

7) Utilize more than one self-defense technique. If you know ten or twelve possible defense moves, you are more thoroughly armed to deal with an attack.

8) Look the attacker in the eyes. Don't turn your back toward him and don't look at the ground. Always remember that your upper body and head are the most important areas to protect. Therefore, don't duck your head. Also, by looking the attacker in the eyes, you are likely to be more able to give a detailed description to the police.

9) Remain forceful yet calm. React immediately. Show the attacker that it was a mistake to molest you of all people. Practice defense techniques either alone or with friends, so that you can handle yourself and in an emergency you won't have to stop to consider what to do.

10) Don't depend on others. You are the only one who can defend yourself. The woman who is used to being defended by others is vulnerable in every situation, and especially when she is called upon to defend herself.

All this discussion about being attacked is rather grim, certainly. It is meant as a practical guide, and you should not begin to expect to encounter an attacker lurking behind every corner; that would needlessly raise your pulse rate and take all the fun out of running.

Take heart in the fact that in some high-crime areas such as New York's Central Park, rapes of runners have actually dropped, due in large part to the presence of large numbers of runners and others using the park.

Dogs: Sharks of the Earth

Although the dog is reputed to be man's best friend, it can be a runner's worst enemy.

The frequency of runners on the roads since the late 1970s has somewhat improved the situation relative to dogs. When runners were rare, they were intruders in the dog's carefully laid out territory, and the dog often played havoc with the lone runner. With the frequency of runners passing through the very territorial dog's turf (or at least near it), many usually vicious dogs have become somewhat resigned to the strange behavior of that species of human being known as the runner.

When dealing with dogs, however, a little caution goes a long way. Always assume when approaching a dog that it *could* attack. No matter how friendly it appears to be, keep in mind that an enthusiastic dog may be more dangerous to you than a vicious dog: the vicious dog has probably been taught to respect human beings by being confronted by them in the past, whereas the enthusiastic dog has often been encouraged to continue being enthusiastic, and enthusiasm or playfulness can easily knock you down when you're in mid-stride, often causing more injuries than an outright attack.

Also remember that a dog is a hunter and chaser, and as a result will often let you pass and then—often silently—will attack from behind.

I have been witness to several incidents where dog owners actually commanded their dogs to attack runners. My defense against such stone-age mentality is a custom-made T-shirt that reads: "My lawyer is more vicious than your dog." If a dog comes at you, stand your ground and command it to "Get lost!" in an authoritative voice, or better yet pick up something and throw it at him: a vicious dog will back off from the thrown object while a playful dog will likely go fetch it.

Sprays to ward off attacks are often useless against dogs because they move rather quickly and circle well, and you may end up spraying into the wind and incapacitating yourself instead of the dog. Sprays have been known to be effective against rapists, however.

Where dogs are concerned, it is important to learn to judge the reaction of a dog to your approach by the dog's actions. Don't show any fear and stare the animal directly in the eyes; dogs have been conditioned for eons to react to commands from humans.

The ultimate defense against dogs is to have your own dog —preferably a *large* dog—go running with you. The *enemy* dog will always perceive your dog as the opponent, and will vent its anger on your dog and not on you.

A Very Few Words on the Greatest Menace

The automobile.

The runner's greatest enemy.

It is bigger than you, it is faster than you, and in the wrong hands, it is extremely deadly.

Some do's and don'ts in dealing with automobiles:

1) *Do* respect the fact that when you are running on a road or highway, you are sharing the roadway with the cars; the roads were built specifically for cars and not all drivers feel you have a right to be out there competing with them.

2) *Do* wear light-colored clothing when running near traffic, especially at dawn and dusk; at night, wear something reflective.

3) *Do* observe all traffic signals and signs.

4) *Do* try to avoid running near traffic whenever possible, both to cut the risk of being hit but also to cut the risk of breathing in the generous amount of exhaust fumes that hang above and near the roadways.

5) *Do* show a bit of courtesy to drivers; they are people, too; and a little courtesy from a runner often leaves a very good impression with a driver that may carry over to the next time that driver encounters a runner.

And on the other side of the coin:

1) *Don't* antagonize drivers. The roads were constructed—in most cases with funds coming from gasoline taxes—to accommodate their cars. As a runner you have no right to disrupt automobile traffic.

2) *Don't* run in the same direction as traffic; run against traffic whenever possible (this is the law in many states) so you can see the on-coming drivers and so they can see you more clearly; make eye contact with on-coming drivers: It will often give you a hint as to what they are going to do so that you can take evasive action.

3) *Don't* run on the road when there is a convenient bike lane or bike path or walking path nearby—you're only increasing your chances of having a very negative experience.

4) *Don't* ignore traffic signals and signs. Just because you are a pedestrian does not give you the right to ignore traffic signs; as a pedestrian, you are still considered traffic and you have certain obligations.

5) *Don't* purposely taunt drivers and *don't ever* assume that a driver sees you. A driver is looking for other vehicular traffic and not for runners. And remember that an obnoxious runner can put a driver in a bad mood, and perhaps the next runner he encounters may become the target of his anger just because *you* were unnecessarily rude. I've seen runners act like pompous asses when running near traffic, as though the world is supposed to stop in its rotation to accommodate their passing. Don't be so stupid—put yourself behind the wheel of the car that didn't see you coming around the corner of that building. What would your reaction be to some half-dressed jerk running out in front of your bumper? A little common courtesy goes a long way. I may be the next runner a driver you've antagonized runs into (literally), and I don't relish the thought of ending up in a hospital for eight weeks to pay for your discourtesy. Let's share the road with motorists as good neighbors.

In Conclusion

Very simply put: Safety is a matter of making maximum use of common sense.

And let's return to the discussion with which this chapter began: Run in groups when possible, both because it is more sociable and enjoyable, and because as you run through our modern world, there is strength in numbers.

SIX:
SPORTSWEAR
AND
HUMAN
PHYSIOLOGY

In the February 1981 issue of *Test* magazine, results of sports underwear were published which had been gathered by an Austrian consumer information agency. The tested sportswear consisted of either pure cotton, pure silk, polyester/cotton, polyester/angora (wool), or wool/polyacryl/angora. The materials were tested to determine how well they kept their shape and how they retained and absorbed heat.

Cotton scored much more poorly in the assessment of absorbency than its reputation would lead you to believe. Silk scored much more favorably. Silk did not keep its shape very well, even though the silk items were washed by hand in this test. For the evaluation of heat retention, some of the products with a mixture of wool received only "average" marks, although wool creates the impression of being a warm material.

These test results clearly show that the material alone does not offer any information about the product's durability and expected comfort. Although labels tell the consumer much about an article of clothing (its composition and cleaning instructions), they do not provide the specific characteristics that determine the product's durability and heat retention.

Many people still believe that clothing made of natural fibers are good and clothing made of synthetic fibers are bad. This notion is false, if viewed objectively. It is now possible to manufacture well-designed clothing out of almost any kind of fiber, including synthetic materials.

WHICH STANDARDS MUST SPORTSWEAR MEET?

This question brings forth two divergent viewpoints. One viewpoint states that the material must absorb moisture efficiently in order to draw sweat from the skin. Natural fibers such as cotton, wool and specially designed (dunova) synthetic fibers all fulfill this requirement.

An opposing school of thought views the ability of a fabric to absorb moisture as being less important. Rather, a good system to transport the moisture is deemed critical, not to hold the moisture given off by the skin, but to allow it to pass out into the environment. This requirement is met by synthetic fibers such as polyester and polypropylene. Tightly worn sportswear must also offer skin-sensitive characteristics. Our skin feels the characteristics of clothing—not only whether the clothing is too tight, scratches, clings or sticks to sweaty skin, but also whether it is soft or smooth, and whether it allows the wearer to move about comfortably. For example, when wool textiles are worn directly on the skin, they are often irritating because they induce itching.

In addition, the piecing together of or the finishing of a textile changes the characteristic qualities of a fiber. In some easy-to-wash or water-resistant wool or cotton outfits, for example, the clothing's ability to absorb moisture will be ruined to a large extent (as with woolen overcoats). Suitable sportswear should have the ability to draw sweat from the skin, pass it outward and then dry off. It should also be temperature balanced by drying the skin, containing body heat and possessing good heat retention in cold weather. Besides having these wear properties, sportswear should also offer good skin-sensitive properties. It should not constrict, scratch or show signs of moisture. In addition, it should maintain its shape and be easy to clean.

THE INTERACTION OF BODY-CLIMATE-CLOTHING

Clothing physiology concerns itself with the interaction between the human body, the climate and the function of clothing. In order to understand the characteristics of clothing, one must consider more closely the interaction between the body, climate, and clothing more closely.

While a person sitting quietly generates 100 watts of heat, this figure climbs to approximately 350 watts during a walk of about three miles per hour; an athlete will reach up to 1000 watts during a peak performance. In order to maintain the body's internal temperature of 98.6 degrees Fahrenheit, the same amount of heat must be expelled as is produced. Ten percent of the produced heat is given off by breathing. The remaining 90 percent must escape from the skin's surface through the clothing. The skin, then, is one of the most important organs for the regulation of body temperature. This fact explains why poorly designed clothing will transport steam and heat from the body's surface to the outside. As in running, when more sweat is produced than can evaporate, the sportswear must be able to absorb it. In order for the desired cooling process to succeed via sweating, it is assumed that the produced sweat can also evaporate and not run off along the skin.

How well this sweat evaporation functions depends heavily on the transportation of moisture and sweat from the clothing.

In any case, it is difficult for clothing to be appropriate for constantly changing environmental conditions: With clothing and the air temperature being equal, a runner can both freeze and sweat, as when we start a slow, long run and gradually increase our pace. Good sportswear, then, must be able to regulate such conditions within reason.

THE THERMOPHYSIOLOGICAL EFFECT OF CLOTHING

It is wrong to think that only thick textiles, especially wool, will produce a high heat retention, as opposed to thinner textiles made of synthetic fibers. The actual heat retainer of the clothing is not the fiber itself, but the enclosed air created by the fiber's construction. The thicker this layer of air is, the greater the retention of heat. Fiber has 1/100th the heat retention of air. A thin, tightly woven design with a higher portion of fiber and flat surfaces provides only slight retention of heat; this kind of design is thus more suitable for warm climates. Designs which allow for a large retention of air as a result of special spinning, weaving or knitting techniques, have a high degree of heat retention.

THE ONION SKIN PRINCIPLE

A prerequisite for a textile's effective heat insulation is that the air trapped in the pores is also contained. For example, a strong wind will rush into the pores of clothing and drastically reduce its heat insulation. As a contrast, clothing will have an appreciably higher heat insulation in a windless room. Even very mild air movement, like that created by an air conditioner, will lower the heat insulation in clothing considerably. Therefore, you should follow the so-called "onion skin principle" in cold or very windy weather—use many layers of different articles of clothing. Individual items can then be worn for a specific purpose—wind or raingear, for example.

This onion skin principle serves two functions: It retains heat, and gives the wearer flexibility in varying weather conditions. The clothing shouldn't inhibit the free exchange of moisture. It should allow you to sweat freely and permit the sweat to evaporate from your body, so that you aren't drenched with sweat after a workout.

During long distance running we have a big advantage if we can adapt the heat insulation of our sportswear to our specific needs. According to the design of our sportswear—turtlenecks with zippers, hooded jackets with drawstring, Velcro or even rolled up sleeves—we can increase the exchange of the warmer air next to the body and the colder environment's air. This airing effect is called ventilation. Ventilation is the most effective means of controlling the heat insulation of clothing.

NATURAL OR SYNTHETIC FIBERS?

In the United States, cotton T-shirts are still preferred by most runners. Very few stores offer T-shirts containing synthetic fibers. Most T-shirts are a combination of polyester and cotton. What follows are descriptions of the wear qualities of synthetic materials. If, after wearing a T-shirt made of synthetic material, you still prefer that favorite cotton T-shirt, by all means wear the cotton. Ultimately, you must decide what works best for you.

During easier workouts in which you will not sweat much, an absorbent cotton jersey or T-shirt can be comfortable. Unfortunately, heavy sweating alters the construction of the cotton. The subsequent swelling of cotton fibers reduces the jersey's permeability, thus inhibiting the transportation of moisture and heat. Since the cotton fibers release the absorbed moisture very slowly and the heat insulation is reduced in wet conditions, this can produce "moist cover" on the skin, and an unpleasant chill as well. If you don't change clothes immediately in such a situation, as is often the case in fun-runs, you face the danger of catching cold because of hypothermia (overcooling).

To reduce your susceptibility to hypothermia, you can wear T-shirts made of synthetic fibers, which are better than other T-shirts because of their superior ability to transport moisture. These shirts move the sweat more quickly from the skin and can maintain a dry layer between the skin and the shirt. You can further protect yourself by keeping warm after finishing your run. Avoid remaining outside with sweaty clothes on after your run. Either put on another layer before stretching or socializing, or go inside to shower right away.

The widespread skepticism that still exists surrounding the comfort of synthetic fabrics is not warranted. West German runner Charlotte Koebke describes the advantages of Dunova, a relatively new synthetic fiber. Although this particular material might not be available in your area, its qualities still hold true, to a certain extent, for other synthetic sportswear. "I believe Dunova is the fabric runners should wear," Koebke says. "I do not feel the sweat-induced dampness, the air passes through it freely, and my back remains dry after a long run. It does not produce an unpleasant odor as a result of the sweat, so that the shirt does not need daily washing. If you run longer distances, cotton shirts often rub under the arms. This is not the case with Dunova. Actually, I am usually skeptical and not so easily impressed, but this material convinced me of its value."

How does Dunova differ from other materials? The Dunova fiber is made up of a net consisting of many tiny canals. These canals absorb the sweat from the skin and quickly move it out to the clothing's surface, where it can evaporate. The absorbed water is "hidden" in the pore system of the fiber. Since water is imperceptible in the pore system, Dunova products can absorb a lot of sweat without beginning to feel wet. Do not use a softener on this kind of product, as it will weaken the absorbency of the material.

SPORTS CLOTHES ON THE MARKET

Textile manufacturing often mixes natural and synthetic fibers for two reasons: to meet the consumer demand for natural fabrics, and to improve the quality of the textiles. Dunova, for example, is manufactured mostly with wool or cotton. There is a mixture of 50 percent angora and 50 percent Trevira on the market under the label Angostar. Runners will be interested in Angostar if they prefer to wear natural fibers without sacrificing the quality of a shirt that is still comfortable when the wearer perspires. In Angostar shirts the Trevira thread is manufactured by a new spinning method so that the thread does not come in contact with the skin. The skin only comes in contact with the angora fiber, which is vastly superior to all other natural fibers in terms of its absorption and release of moisture.

The manufacturer of Angostar has stated that its clothing can also be worn on sensitive skin, since no more itching will occur after two washings. Angostar can be washed at 140 degrees Fahrenheit and then spun-dry, without losing its fit.

PERSONAL EXPERIENCES WITH DIFFERENT KINDS OF SPORTSWEAR

In order to obtain a personal impression of the wear qualities and washing requirements of sportswear, I ran alternately in a T-shirt or turtleneck made of Dunova, and poly-

propylene. Normally, I run six miles in just under one hour. After the run, I always drive home immediately and change clothes. In this fashion, I always protect myself against the danger of colds which could result from cooling off.

In order for me to better compare and judge these materials, I didn't change right after the runs, but rather, kept the clothes on for a few hours. Based purely on the wear qualities of the materials, I preferred Dunova, because this material felt comfortable during both hot and cool days, where I only felt comfortable in cool weather while wearing Angostar and polypropylene. In any case, I can't confirm Mrs. Koebke's impression that Dunova limits the amount of body odor caused by sweating. This was more my impression of Angostar. Regarding the wash care, these textiles are not only easy to clean, but also colorfast. My Dunova test shirt Medico faded, and in this respect did not meet my expectations.

My Ron Hill's Lady Shirt (100 percent nylon) convinced me how little a role the fibers themselves play in determining the comfort of a fabric. I wore this shirt on the few really hot summer days. This shirt kept me cool through its sewn-on netting, which made the running easier for me on hot days.

For women who prefer not to run in shorts, I looked for a pair of light warmup pants that were also comfortable to wear on warm days. As an active runner in the 1960s, I wore such pants. They were made of pure cotton and were sold under the brand name "Sweden Pants." They did not completely meet my expectations, but were noticeably more comfortable to wear than the synthetic gymnastics pants.

I felt that the Lifa sportswear from Helly Hansen (made of polypropylene) was comfortable on cool days. My running partner wears this material in winter under her training suit and is very satisfied with it. I can also recommend Helly Hansen's cold-weather jackets that have fur lining both inside and outside, with a lengthened backside as protection for the kidneys and extra-long sleeves. This jacket is made of a light, water-resistant material and retains heat well as a result of the insulated layer of air. At first I had misgivings about this jacket; I thought that I would begin to sweat uncomfortably in it after only a few miles. Yet when I wore only this jacket over a T-shirt in a drizzling rain, I was impressed with its wear and comfort. The dampness did not penetrate the jacket—my skin remained dry and warm. I also did not break out into an uncomfortable sweat. The lengthened sleeves kept my hands warm even without gloves. This jacket is also practical for running, because it replaces articles of clothing that otherwise would have to be worn over one another in wet or cold weather. After I washed this jacket, it dried very quickly, did not fade and kept its shape after the wash. The only item that I felt this jacket lacked was head protection in the form of a removable hood.

GETTING DOWN TO BASICS

As long as you wear dependable shoes, you probably won't have many problems with clothes. Keep comfort and simplicity in mind, above all else. Running clothes need not be expensive. A favorite old T-shirt and gym shorts might be better than flashy, new stuff if they are comfortable. However, you should be concerned about chafing. Remember, you are planning to sweat hard and get very dirty in your running outfits. Don't set out in something you don't want to soil.

The woman runner's bare essentials are a T-shirt or tank top, running shorts, and if she needs one, a good support bra. Clothing should not be so tight that it binds or causes chafing, particularly under the arms, in the crotch and on the inside of the thighs. Cotton is always a good choice of fabric, since it absorbs perspiration well, but some women prefer soft nylon, which reduces chafing. Underwear should be cotton or at least have a cotton panel crotch to absorb moisture and help prevent vaginal infection. Remember to dress in layers when running. Articles can be removed or added as your body or the air temperature changes.

Use this checklist when shopping for running wear:

Shorts. Any comfortable shorts will do; the basic men's

cotton variety are cheaper than those sold for women in specialty shops. The problem with men's shorts is that many styles just don't fit women properly—they're either too short or too big in the waist, tight in the hips, high-cut or they may ride up when you run. Try different styles to find one that fits well. Be sure to study them from all angles in a fitting-room mirror and bend over to touch your toes. You should be able to do this without feeling an uncomfortable pull in your crotch and without exposing your backside.

Make sure that the waistband on your shorts does not roll or pinch, and look for seams that won't chafe your legs. If you want to invest in shorts designed especially for runners, there are many on the market with outside seams (completely eliminating any possibility of chafing), side slits for movement and even little Velcro pockets to keep an apartment key and identification card handy.

Shirts. As mentioned, most runners make do with a basic cotton T-shirt, but there are others from which to choose. Moving Comfort, Inc. in Arlington, Va., makes shirts just for women, with ventilating fabric at the waist and tank tops with straps cut wide enough to hide a bra. Many other companies now include similar sportswear in their lines. Remember to consider color when choosing a shirt in which to run. Wear white to reflect as much heat as possible, yellow and orange for runs at dusk or on overcast days so you can be easily seen by motorists. Never wear a dark color for a night run.

Bras. The amount of support you need from a bra depends on your build. Small-breasted women may be comfortable running braless; large-breasted women may want to invest in a good running bra. The key is comfort—if it feels right it's probably right for you. In general, women who wear B-cup bras or larger will probably want to wear one while running to prevent uncomfortable bouncing. There are a variety of good running bras on the market today from which to choose. Many are designed without seams, hooks or snaps for a smooth line and maximum comfort—since the last thing a woman runner needs is sharp metal poking into her skin as she runs. It's possible to find bras that double as shirts—SLS Inc., in Burlington, Vt., makes "Jogbra," a halter-top-like garment that comes in a variety of colors and provides sufficient support.

One alternative to bras that many women have found satisfactory is a dancer's leotard. These are snug enough to offer support but are not constricting. Leotards are available in a variety of styles, including long-sleeved, short-sleeved, and sleeveless designs.

Sweat suits, warm ups. You can pay a fortune for a fancy "jogging suit." Wait until someone gives you one for Christmas. Meanwhile, shop the boys' departments at discount stores and you'll find what you need at the right price. Basic gray sweats will cost little. Look for special features like pockets, hoods and drawstring waists.

Windbreaker. If you plan to run in the rain (and if you're serious about running, there's no way to avoid it), a waterproof windbreaker is practically a necessity. Make sure it's lightweight and either bright-colored or trimmed with reflective tape. (Rainstorms and darkness tend to go hand-in-hand.)

Ideally, rain gear should not only be waterproof from the outside to the inside, but should simultaneously provide moisture-permeability from the inside to the outside. Gore-Tex is a jacket that provides these features. The special characteristics of Gore-Tex—waterproof, windproof and air permeable—are a result of the jacket's micropore membranes. Since a water drop is 20,000 times larger than a Gore-Tex membrane pore, the Gore-Tex products are waterproof and windproof, but easily allow steam or body moisture to pass from the body surface to the outside. As rain gear, then, Gore-Tex articles offer a substantially better degree of comfort than the conventional windbreakers.

Hat. Hats are an important part of the runner's wardrobe, especially under extreme weather conditions. In very cold weather you should never run without a hat, since approximately 50 percent of the body's heat can be lost through the top of the head. In winter, wear a wool knit ski-cap that will cover your ears. On very cold days, you might want to try a ski mask with openings for the eyes and nose. Summer hats are usually the visor variety—something to keep the strong summer sun off the top of the head and out of the eyes. Any baseball cap will do.

These are the bare essentials of the runner's wardrobe. Specialty shops and department stores are full of additional items to wear while running, but if your budget is tight, this list should meet all of your needs.

If you have a problem with finding the proper size and just can't make do with inexpensive men's clothing, there are many companies that either specialize in women's running garments or manufacture a women's line. You can write or call any of these stores to find the outlet nearest your home.

SEVEN: PROPER SHOE SELECTION WARDS OFF INJURIES

According to current research, one out of eight beginning runners gets injured. That's an alarming statistic. The most critical period is the first six weeks of a running program. Overexertion is often the cause of common injuries; one runs either too fast or too much. Another prime cause is poorly constructed athletic shoes that may not even be designed for running. All too often, novices begin their running programs wearing tennis or basketball shoes, which are not designed to absorb the stresses that running places on the musculoskeletal structure.

In general, women aren't injured as often as men. They do, however, suffer more knee and calf injuries than men, according to the findings of Dr. John W. Pagliano, a prominent podiatrist in Long Beach, Calif.

One of the most exhausting surveys on this subject was done of 1366 men and 119 women who were participating in extensive exercise drills over an eight-week period at the U.S. Military Academy in West Point, N.Y. After the testing period, 5 percent of the men, and an astonishing 26 percent of the women were injured. During the course of the eight weeks, 7.7 percent of the men and 21 percent of the women were hospitalized because of illness, injury or exhaustion. During this same period, 1 percent of the men and 10 percent of the women developed stress fractures as determined by five orthopedic specialists. Finally, West Point doctors concluded that the cardiovascular strengths of men and women were comparable.

Stress fractures are fairly common among women runners, and are commonly treated incorrectly in the initial stages of the injury. Reddening and swelling point toward a tendon injury, and the typical treatments—massage, ice and ointments—are prescribed. An X-ray usually reveals nothing. The stress fracture will first become visible as a callus after three weeks, reports Dr. Steve Subotnick, a podiatrist from Hayward, Calif. Subotnick recorded cases after seven weeks when the injury first became visible. When the injury is finally recognized for what it is, a minimum of three weeks rest is usually prescribed. Depending on which bones are affected, the foot will be placed in a cast. Running is, of course, impossible, although riding a stationary bike is sometimes allowed. When the cast is removed, swimming is a good way to regain some of the lost conditioning without stressing the injured bones.

Subotnick recommends soft-soled shoes with good shock absorption properties for athletes susceptible to stress fractures. There is a bit of good news for women who suffer a stress fracture. The injured bone usually heels so well that it probably won't cause any further problems.

FALLEN AND HIGH ARCHES

Two of the most common foot anomalies are fallen and high arches. According to Subotnick, who has an index of more than 4000 athletes, fallen arches occur in 40 percent of the population and high arches in 20 to 25 percent. The rest have normal feet. That isn't any consolation to those stuck with fallen arches, which are characterized by flatness over the entire foot and a tendency for the foot to turn inward (pronation).

For this problem, Subotnick recommends a shoe with a firm heel cup that will offer the foot a firm hold in this vitally important part of the shoe. Subotnick is adamantly opposed to shoes with air soles. He believes they're too soft. Instead, Subotnick recommends a relatively hard sole.

In one of Subotnick's cases, a flat-footed athlete started running and bruised his heel quite badly. After a few years of coping with this injury, the runner became a forefoot striker, which strengthened his arches. Subotnick explained, "The quicker pace of running on the forefoot helps correct supination (when a person's foot rolls outward upon impact), and moves the heel away from the ground."

That a lifting of the arch can occur even during a marathon has been demonstrated in research done by G. Brueggeman and W. Koring, who examined twenty-seven women marathoners before and after runs. These runners were between eighteen and fifty-nine years old (average age of forty-two) and averaged eighty-eight miles a week. On average they weighed 120 pounds, and were five-feet, four-inches tall. Each trained up to 15 percent of the time in the forest, on asphalt, or on a variety of surfaces.

Foot impressions were taken with a podometer of a forefoot striker in which the curvature of the arch was measured. The result of the examination revealed that in all cases the runners' arches lifted—more noticeably with women who had more pronounced fallen arches. Both doctors concluded that, contrary to the prevailing notion that the arch falls during a run, the arch actually lifts up during intensive running.

According to Subotnick, runners with high arches shouldn't plant their forefoot too forcefully. Many runners and especially women with high arches tend to run on the balls of their feet. Doing so makes them more susceptible to stress fractures. Such runners require a shoe with a lower heel counter, providing them more freedom of movement. Since the toe region is often subjected to a pinching kind of action, the toes also need a lot of room.

Dr. Sigrid Schmidt, of West Germany, started running in 1978. She immediately began to suffer from a swelling of the joints in both ankles. She lost three toenails because her shoes were too tight. The following year, after a hike, she experienced severe pain in the calves. Her difficulties—symptomatic of hallux valgus—disappeared two years later. Why? Dr. Schmidt reported, "I was able to stretch and straighten the hallux valgus. All of the toes can be individually stretched, especially the small toes."

Hallux valgus is a mispositioning of the big toe, which can actually push under the other toes in extreme cases. This

Dr. Steve Subotnick, a podiatrist, has treated thousands of athletes.

condition includes the formation of pronounced bunions and can be remedied with the purchase of a shoe with a roomy toe box. Hallux valgus will worsen if the runner wears narrow, pointed shoes.

MOVING DOWN FROM HIGH HEELS

Women runners, even those with so-called normal feet, should stop wearing high-heeled shoes. They cause an unhealthy shortening of the Achilles tendon and cause the calf muscles to atrophy. Stiletto heels can also damage the hips. Women who run at night after a long day of wearing high heels, run a high risk of injuries because of this shortening of the tendon and calf.

With Achilles tendon problems such as severe tendinitis, a temporary, minor elevation (using small foam wedges or heel pads) of the foot can help. Another recommendation is to avoid soft shoes in which the foot sinks into the sole. Look for firm shoes and run on a flat, firm surface (avoid sand).

Knee injuries are also common. There is the Hoffaschen Syndrome which usually runs its course and disappears on its own after just a few days of soreness. Most people can run through this inflammation of the Hoffaschen fatty tissue. It's been shown that a faster run puts less strain on the knee than an appreciably slower run because the support phases of the knee are shorter. In contrast to a runner with Achilles tendon problems, who should wear a harder-soled shoe, a runner who suffers knee injuries should wear soft shoes with a substantial elevation in the heel area and run on softer, yielding surfaces.

DEMANDS PLACED ON RUNNING SHOES

From the previous explanation, it follows that the experienced female runner should have more than one pair of running shoes at her disposal. A good idea would be to have one with soft soles, another pair with hard soles and yet another for running on trails. You might also want to add a pair of lighter weight racing flats. You should also take into consideration that with daily training in damp weather, it takes a day or so for a wet pair to dry. So wearing several different pairs of shoes serves an important function: Minor injury problems often disappear if you simply change shoes every day. In contrast, a well-known German runner took only one pair of training shoes on a running vacation in 1982 in order to save room in the suitcase. She said, "I quickly became injured. I won't make that mistake again."

The New Balance 660 is one of many shoes in the highly competitive shoe market.

Fundamentally, a running shoe should have a three-layer sole construction: midsole, heel wedge and running sole. A polyurethane sole won't have the same cushioning effect that a three-layer sole will offer. Likewise, foot strikes can't be absorbed over as long a period of time, since the polyurethane is more affected by temperature changes than a three-layer construction, and will eventually harden. The glues that are now being used guarantee that the soles won't come apart as they once did. But the gluing lengthens the production time and increases the price of the shoe.

Air chambers in the midsoles can add cushioning, but are overrated. They aren't like a hovercraft. You should also be mindful of midsoles that are too soft. One of the primary drawbacks to soft midsole materials is that they weaken quicker than harder ones; thus the sole will collapse and the cushioning effect will be lost.

As a material for uppers, leather is losing some of its appeal, although it's still the least irritating material to the skin. Multi-laminated materials have established themselves in running shoes today. They are lighter and allow the foot to breathe more easily with mesh.

The insoles usually consist of a removable inlay that can be replaced by an orthotic device that compensates for more severe foot anomalies. The inner edge of the insole is often elevated in order to move the foot upward. In one of the new Brooks shoes, the entire inner sole is 4 percent higher than the outer sole, which is especially helpful to runners with fallen arches or with knock-knees. But the person who is bow-legged runs on the edge of these shoes and thus has poor stability. Such a bow-legged runner would also wear down the hardest heel cups after only a short period of running.

A big difference exists between the related shoe lasts. Since women have narrower feet than men, they should take special care to buy snug-fitting shoes. Wearing wide shoes would make them more susceptible to twisted ankles. Most of the Adidas models are narrowly constructed. Other narrow shoes include models from Asics Tiger and Karhu, while Puma is built somewhat wider. New Balance offers shoes in three widths. When a variety of widths are not available, runners tend to buy a larger size. Persons with narrower feet are forced to buy smaller shoes. Blisters and black toenails often result if the shoes are too tight. Thus, you should make certain the shoe offers a 1/2-thumb width of extra space for your toes. That's because your feet will swell when warmed up. A shoe that's too large can be used when wearing extra socks or inserts, but a shoe that's too small is useless.

You should expect a good running shoe to cost at least as much (if not more) as a good dress shoe. The least expensive recommended running shoe costs about $40 to $50. Shoes of the highest quality can cost up to $100. There are even shoes today that exceed $150.

Running shoes that match your particular needs provide the best means of preventing injuries. Another risk will decrease if you divide training sessions into four parts: stretching, warmup, the actual workout and warmdown. Additional preventive measures would include warm sulfur baths, saunas, judicious use of ice, and regular massages.

Despite all these precautions, you can still develop running injuries. Even experienced runners, such as Rosemarie Fricker, can get hurt. And when they do it's not always easy finding doctors with running expertise. Fricker met with an orthopedist in West Germany to ask him about a running injury she had. Fricker asked if she could continue running during her treatment and the doctor replied, "If you have such a large family, you certainly have enough work at home. You don't need to run around outside, too."

EIGHT: THE PSYCHOLOGICAL BENEFITS OF RUNNING

In the world of running, as in mathematics, nursing and other professional pursuits, women have had to rise up and free themselves of oppression. There are many factors and events that could document women's gradual progression into running as a sport and lifestyle, but the intention here is to show the psychological roadways women have chosen to travel in order to break new ground.

Why has it taken women so long to break through to the other side of psychological oppression—to positivism and actuality? The primary reason is that in the past, women for the most part have discovered their identities through the eyes of their parents (as children) and through men (as adults). Their sources of power and autonomy have been found in the philosophies of others— not from a center located inside themselves.

From early on, young girls begin to cultivate the expectations of those around them. For instance, up until a decade ago some of the traits admired in girls have been passivity, non-competitiveness, fragility and looking attractive (as opposed to being bright, creative or physically fit). But whatever adjectives women have allowed themselves to be defined by, the result remains the same: For survival's sake, young girls have understood the importance of remaining unthreatening to the social, political and athletic worlds spinning around them.

Many women have had a difficult time dealing with the various myths of the woman runner. I wonder how many "popular" girls grew up joking about the female athletes they ignored in school. How many times have women athletes been alluded to as "butches," "dykes" and "spinsters"? Who were these muscular loners who strove for physical fitness and how did they move past the stereotypes that have so impressed our lives?

In any oppressed group of people there will always be individuals who break out and follow their own instincts and dreams. These are people who are willing to go against traditional modes of behavior in order to nurture change, and people who are governed by their own wills rather than by the wishes of others. Possibly they are from families who have admired other athletic members, or they are individuals who are naturally inclined toward athletics because of their physical stature. Whatever their backgrounds, they are people who are not afraid to make mistakes and turn around and learn from them. But most of all, they are people who are as responsive to their own aspirations and needs as they are to those of their parents, husbands, children and friends.

Recently, women have taken it upon themselves to redefine femininity inside of the athletic world. They are learning that many of the traits that are considered male apply to their own psyches as well. That's when they become independent enough to trust their own feelings.

It is of primary importance for every woman who wants to run to dispel the myths that surround her. It is imperative that she knows her body is built for endurance and that fragility is a mindset and not a physiological state. She must believe that she has the ability to learn by taking directions, criticism and support—that her motor skills are adaptable, and that she may sustain injuries but can recover from them.

On a sexual level, there are myths perpetuated regarding the loss of softness, problems with child-bearing, a general disinterest in men and a more "controlling spirit." Statistics show that physical fitness and exercise can facilitate child-bearing and does tone the musculature of women. These facts should be welcome to any healthy woman. As for interest in men, psychologists feel that women turn to men for what they *want* rather than what they *need* when their self-

esteem is heightened. And, yes, they do ask for an equal proportioning of control within the sexual and emotional domain. In short, they begin to ask for their fair share.

Once a woman has decided to run, she must make the commitment to run through the uncertainty and fear that surface simultaneously. This is new turf, and if she is a person who has spent most of her time in the company of others, she may need to learn to be alone—in fact, learn to *like* being alone.

This is a tremendously difficult process, because many women are taught from day one that their most important role is that of the supportive bystander or the nurturing mother. She may feel her identity lies in igniting energy in others. In other words, to make a commitment to running—fully incorporating it into her lifestyle—a woman must learn to separate her world and her identity. And because her world has been defined by countless others (who depend on her), she may experience a modicum of guilt.

So, it becomes a question of usurping time and spending it on herself. It is a process of letting those persons with whom she has professional and personal relationships know that she has acquired her walking (in this case, "running") papers. She must be able to persevere past all of the shifting of responsibilities, the emotional overlays and the worry that possibly she isn't really doing the "right" thing. In the beginning, the woman runner can come up with ten good reasons not to run for every reason in favor of it. And there will always be someone in the crowd to back those anxieties.

Once she has freed herself of everyone else's demands and expectations, she is ready to face her own, and when an individual faces a new world without the supportive ties to which she has been accustomed, a second powerful emotion arises: fear.

As she begins her run she learns the inner workings of a whole new emotional territory. The mind's questions are a deft trickery, sometimes producing weariness and doubt. How long should she run? Where should she go? Is it safe to run alone? Can she really stand the pain? What if she gets lost? What if she can't *really* go the distance?

But, on the other side of this psychological coin . . . what if she really *can* go the distance? What doors could this possibly open? How might she gain?

Inherent in this fear of failure/fear of success mechanism lies a far more powerful emotional property—courage. When it comes down to the real acid test, a woman who wants to run will transcend any obstacle that blocks her way. She knows in her intuitive and instinctive areas that the commitment she is beginning to make will change her life forever and her newfound curiosity begins to welcome these changes.

So she begins to run in an organized, consistent manner. And as she runs, the positive aspects of self-worth begin to emerge: Soon she discovers determination, discipline, independent thinking, perseverance, patience and peace of mind. She discovers that running allows her a space and time to grow into the person she has secretly wanted to become all along.

NINE: NATURAL CARE FOR THE SKIN AND BODY

The skin is the largest organ of your body. It is directly exposed to the environment and reacts most to environmental conditions. In the process, the skin serves us not only as protection against harmful influences from the outside, but is also directly involved in the body's metabolism, as well as blood and lymph systems. Our skin is also an important sense organ that perceives stimuli such as pain, cold and warmth. But stimuli are also passed through the skin from the inside; for example, excitement causes the skin to either redden or turn white. An unhealthy lifestyle and insufficient sleep will cause you to appear tired and unhealthy. In running, our skin plays the important role of excretory organ and temperature regulator. We can understand the relationship between skin nutrition and overall nutrition only by being aware of the functional relationship between skin and metabolism.

COMPOSITION AND METABOLISM OF THE SKIN

The skin is made up of three separate layers: the subcutis, the dermis and the epidermis. The deepest layer, the subcutis, is made up of loose connective tissue that includes varying amounts of fat cells, and is therefore called subcutis fat tissue. Depending on the number and size of the fat cells, the tissue can vary in thickness from a few millimeters to several centimeters. The nature of the fat tissue in the subcutis is different among men and women. It can appear as cellulite in women, especially in bloated fat cells that aren't supported by the connective tissue.

On top of the subcutis lies the dermis, which is richly supplied with blood and is interlaced with collagen, nerve and muscle fiber. The dermis is directly tied into the circulatory system by the network of blood vessels and in this way takes part in metabolism. The composition of the dermis determines the elasticity of the skin. In young people, a lot of moisture is stored in this layer. As a person ages, his collagen fibers lose their ability to store water and harden. It is very difficult to increase the water content of the dermis by external means.

The layer of epidermis is the skin's contact with the outside world. Among young people, it is firmly attached to the dermis. Certain layers thin out as part of the aging process and the meshing becomes looser.

The deepest layer of the epidermis, known as the germinal layer, meshes with the dermis like a set of interlocking gears. The regeneration or renewal of skin takes place in this germinal layer as the nutrients are supplied into this layer from the inside. New cells form here continuously as a result of cell division, while the old cells are forced to the skin's surface where they harden. This process lasts about twenty-eight days. During this time the epidermis normally renews itself from the cell-building germinal layer to the outermost hardened layer.

We can promote this continual regenerative process through systematic care. An important prerequisite to healthy skin is the internal supply of all the important building blocks (nutrients) from the inner layers. This is only possible through proper nutrition. Another requirement is avoiding substances damaging to the skin, such as nicotine, which shrinks the very smallest capillaries of the skin. Therefore, less oxygen is transported to the cells. The consequences of smoking is poorly fed, tough skin, which ages more quickly as a result. Influencing the skin's metabolism is known as "cosmetics from the inside."

The epidermis has a fatty covering that is formed from the sebaceous and sweat glands of the skin and protects the skin

Olympic marathoner Julie Brown prefers running with her hair cut short.

from drying out. The sebaceous glands are responsible for this protective function. While the sebaceous glands change only slightly among men up to age forty, and then begin to weaken noticeably, the woman's skin becomes dryer from age twenty-five onward. The man's skin, though, will change very little after age sixty. Thus, the woman's sebum level is higher among younger women and lower among older women than men of similar ages. Therefore, women have a great need to keep their skin smooth by using preparations containing fat.

The fat covering develops in connection with the secretion of the sweat glands of the skin's acidic protective layer, which protects against chemical and bacterial growth. The acidity of the skin is measured as a pH value and is normally five to six.

The fat and acid protective layers must be maintained for the protection of the skin. If these protective film layers are washed away, the protective function of the skin is disrupted. What we remove from the skin by washing should be replaced.

WHAT CARE DOES YOUR SKIN NEED?

The secret to keeping your skin healthy is to take care of it on a regular basis, which compensates for the lack of natural protective substances. Regularly treated skin looks fresher and more elastic than neglected skin. Why? There are environmental influences that speed up the aging process, but can be avoided or protected against with specific care. The selection and use of skin care treatments must be made according to your skin type, age and the time of year.

HOW CAN YOU IDENTIFY YOUR SKIN TYPE?

There are certain recognizable characteristics that distinguish the various skin types. Dry skin is very thin and porous, containing very small arteries that tend to be enlarged. The effects of air conditioning, bad air and stress are all more noticeable with this kind of skin. Metabolic disturbances cause red blotches to appear on the skin. As a result of its lower fat and water content, dry skin tends to develop wrinkles and ages more quickly. If you start early with a specific treatment that rebalances the fat and moisture content, you can keep your skin looking beautiful.

FAT AND UNCLEAN SKIN

Greasy skin with enlarged pores, a greasy luster and impurities can be improved markedly by using specific care and nutrition. Many young men and women suffer from unclear skin, pimples and blackheads. Both sweets and greasy and sharply spiced foods can bring on pimples and can worsen the appearance of the skin. In contrast to dry skin, greasy skin is robust and ages more slowly. And with the passing years it alone regulates the excessive sebaceous seceretion.

NORMAL SKIN

Normal skin has very fine pores and is well stretched. It shows neither reddening nor irritation. It is skin without problems. Skin with a mixture of both dry and greasy patches is common, too. The greasy patches are usually located in the so-called T-zone (forehead, nose and chin) while the cheeks and outer lying regions of the face are usually dry.

SKIN CARE

Regardless of which skin type you possess, all facial skin should always be cleaned gently with, for example, a cleansing milk designed for your particular skin type. Moisturizing emulsions are recommended for daily protection against the heat, thus producing a thin, permeable film on the skin that prevents the buildup of heat. In cold weather a cream containing grease protects the skin from a large heat loss. Don't wear any make-up while running, not because the pores may clog up, but because all make-up can become stained.

Your shower or bath gel should be mild enough so that it doesn't weaken the natural layer of fatty acid protecting the

skin. Alternately, apply a moisture-containing body emul-
sion and a good hand oil after a shower, bath or sauna. Skin
oils are well-suited to retaining body heat in winter.

HAIR REMOVAL FOR THE UNDERARMS

In principle, it is recommended to remove hair from the
underarm for hygenic reasons. Immediately after the hair is
removed, skin powder should be used rather than de-
oderant.

SKIN PROTECTION IN TROPICAL COUNTRIES

The adjustment from a moderate climate to a hot zone is a
burden not only for the circulatory system, but also for the
skin. In southern latitudes, the sun shines more intensively
than in northern countries. Every woman should know that
extended sunbathing is harmful to the skin, and encourages
the aging of the connective tissue. Therefore, you should always use effective sun protection. Just as important is a good
pair of sunglasses with high quality lenses. It is not only a
good form of eye protection, but also prevents the formation
of tiny wrinkles around the eyes. When the skin causes problems, that is no reason to put up with it. Today you can do
something specific for many skin problems.

The cosmetics expert and former track and field athlete Li-
selotte Bruder of Duesseldorf has compiled the following list
of practical care tips for *Running For Women:*

Cleaning: Wipe the skin with facial milk and facial lotion
that has a low alcohol content (5 to 10 percent).

Protection: Wear a thin layer of moisturizing cream. Cover
the enlarged blood vessels on the cheek area with a light
camomile cream and avoid intense sun rays or cold weather.
Avoid hot compresses or facial steam baths.

After the run: Shower with a mild shower gel or baby
soap. Remove dust and grease particles from the face with
cleansing lotion. Wash the lotion off with clear, lukewarm
water. For daily care wear a light moisturizing cream containing grease. Conceal enlarged blood vessels with a cover stick

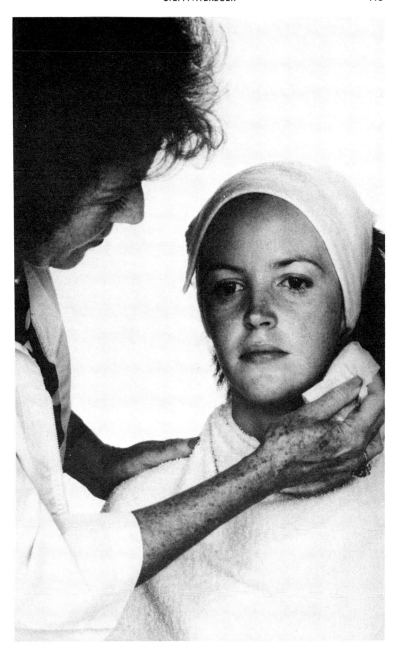

or cream. Eventual make-up should contain little grease. For night care you should wear a light grease cream after washing your face.

Additional care: As a weekly facial, a "do-it-yourself" yogurt mask (among others) is suitable in addition to the ready-made packages.

Preparation: Mix together two tablespoons of low-fat yogurt, one tablespoon of mineral water, one teaspoon of honey, five drops of lemon juice, and apply to your lightly greased skin. Allow it to be absorbed into the skin for fifteen minutes, wash it off without rubbing it and rinse the face with lukewarm water. In addition, use a moisturizing cream as day protection and a light grease cream for nighttime protection.

CARE TIPS FOR GREASY AND UNCLEAN SKIN

Cleaning: Clean with a mild facial milk or alkaline-free soap with a measured pH of 5.5 to 6.0. Clean the face again with a facial lotion containing 20 to 30 percent alcohol. Don't carry out any severe measures to remove grease. An excessive removal of grease from the skin will stimulate the sebaceous glands to produce more grease. Use only emulsions containing moisturizers as day and night protection. Cover skin impurities with an antibacterial cover pencil.

After the run: Cleaning the face is always essential. Hence, you should observe cleanliness fastidiously to disrupt the bacterial growth cycle and to protect the skin from new outbreaks of bacteria. A natural facial with a thicker consistency helps to cover up skin impurities.

Intensive care: Regularly apply cleaning facials intensively in order to remove excessive hardening of skin particles and to shrink the pores. Suitable ready-to-use facial masks include camphor-chlorophyll and enzyme packages.

The "do-it-yourself" yeast facial: Mix yeast bought from a health food store with mineral water and mix them into a spreadable paste.

Almond meal facial: Mix sea sand-almond meal with lukewarm water into a spreadable paste. After the mixture begins to dry, rub it off in the sink with a circular motion.

Mud facial: Mix mud with lukewarm water. Always wear the facial on a lightly creamed skin, allow it to work itself in for fifteen minutes, wash it off and rinse the face well.

WHAT IS MEANT BY BREATHING SKIN?

Many people believe that make-up or powder can hinder the breathing of the skin. These ideas are unfounded, as they are based on the false assumption that the breathing of the skin is the kind of process in which the oxygen could be breathed in through the skin—analogous to the breathing process in the lungs.

You cannot speak of the skin breathing in the normal sense of the word. Breathing of the skin refers to the metabolism within the cells. Like all of the body's cells, the skin cells breathe also. That is, they take in oxygen and give off carbon dioxide. Both gases, however, are transported by the blood and lymphatic systems to the lungs, where the gas exchange can take place. The skin can be neither nourished by the pores, nor can it breath through the pores. We must always view the skin within the context of its interaction with the total organism.

Cosmetic care can promote healthy skin. It cannot, however, slow the natural aging process of the skin, and cannot remove wrinkles. Besides taking care of skin externally, you should also provide the skin with all of the necessary nutrients. The skin's appearance improves with proper nutrition. This is also true if the person avoids alternating between the starvation diets and binge periods.

Excess weight is also a cosmetic problem because fatty deposits are stored in the subcutis. Every drastic starvation diet leads to excessive stretching of the epidermis. The overstretched skin cannot adapt immediately and quickly enough to the changed surface area, since the skin's elasticity has been overextended. This condition leads to excessive wrinkling.

Not only do physical changes affect the skin, but our psychological condition also influences the skin. The skin, then, reflects our inner state. A successful cosmetics treatment thus includes the maintenance of a person's psychological health. In particular, a positive outlook on life, pleasure and relaxation, plus successful experiences and the possibility of self-fulfillment, all have a positive affect on our appearance. Every woman must develop this positive attitude on her own.

HAIR CARE TIPS FOR WOMEN

Healthy, well-kempt hair is not only attractive, but also influences our general well-being. Why else would we spend so much time and energy taking care of our hair? Although running has a positive effect on a woman's body and psyche, the sport sometimes takes its toll on a woman's hairdo. Both short and long hair have their advantages and disadvantages, yet, in general, long hair presents the woman runner with more care problems.

Short hair causes few problems, as it requires little care after washing. I myself have thin hair, which quickly becomes frizzy, even in low humidity or when I sweat. To prevent frizziness, I put my hair up. I also wear a headband so it won't bother me when I run. In spite of my hair problems, I schedule my runs according to my work schedule and not the weather conditions.

There are many women with long hair, however, who simply never run in humid or rainy weather. If these women want to train consistently, they will face difficult problems if they expect their hairdos to remain flawless after showering. If your hair is long, you can take certain preventive measures to reduce the weather's impact on it. A hard training session will result in heavy sweating, bringing about increased oiliness of the hair. By tying your hair up before a run, the hair will not be bothersome and will keep its shape. In order to prevent your hair from becoming too dirty, you should tie it up into a bun. This method will make it difficult for the oil and sweat to work their way into most of your hair.

There are other ways of protecting long hair during runs. Klaus Fischer, who runs a hair salon in Cologne, gives female runners the following advice: "Before a run, women with shoulder-length hair should put their hair into a bun and cover it with a cap or cloth. You should first comb out the hair when it is completely dry. After the run, you should part the hair in the middle or on the side and separate the hair along the hairline down to the neck. You should then tie both halves of the hair with barrettes. This hairdo is most easily done with slightly wet hair. You can also tie up or bind long hair easily, using combs and barrettes to create a stylish hairdo. In addition, you can braid your hair into pigtails, allow them to dry and then comb out with a large-toothed comb. This hairdo is similar to a naturally dried perm. Providing you use a mild shampoo, washing your hair daily will not harm it, regardless of its length or composition. For intensive care I recommend a beauty pack every fourteen days. The treatment is normally washed out after thirty minutes, though it is more effective if left on overnight (under your shower cap, for example). If you use hair setting or lotion for a blow-dryer, you should make sure it does not contain any alcohol, since the alcohol destroys the effectiveness of the beauty pack."

Greasy hair requires different treatment. A representative of the Technical Application Laboratories of the Henkel Co. in Dusseldorf, West Germany, explains: "Greasy hair is basically a skin problem. The hair is greasy because too much oil lies on the scalp." Since the oil is secreted by the sebaceous glands, and all glands are regulated by hormones, you can control oil production with antihormones, although such treatment should be carried out under a physician's care. Washing your hair with a mild shampoo, then, is the most successful measure to take against this widespread and cosmetically unpleasant condition.

You can kill two birds with one stone by wearing a blow-dried perm (tightly curled, when possible). First, no locks of hair will get in your way while you run. Second, if you sweat a lot during a hard workout, the sweat will not affect the hair much, since the hair will not become straggly that easily. You can also use a perm with thin hair. With proper attention, women can still run on a regular basis and keep their hair looking attractive. Long and greasy hair present unique yet solvable care problems. Women with long hair can train consistently in hot or humid weather if they do not expect their hair to look flawless seven days a week. Tying your hair up will limit the amount of oil and sweat that can work its way into the hair. Since greasy hair is caused by an overproduction of the sebaceous glands, antihormones may clear up this condition if taken while under a doctor's supervision. For less severe cases, a mild shampoo may be sufficient.

TEN: STAY HEALTHY THROUGH PROPER NUTRITION

Every person must eat and drink to survive. For all physical activities, we require energy that can only be obtained from food. Each woman's energy requirements are different and depend on her metabolism. This metabolism, in turn, consists of two types: the basal metabolism and the work metabolism.

The basal metabolism is the energy required for the "hidden" metabolic processes that take place in the body. We need energy even while at a complete rest. For example, we need to regulate our breathing, body temperature and functions of the circulatory system. Your basal metabolic rate is influenced by the following factors:

1) Sex: A woman's BMR is 10 percent lower than a man's. This difference is based on the metabolic effect of the sex hormones. In addition, a woman possesses more fatty tissue, which results in a lower metabolic rate.

2) Age: A younger person has a higher BMR than an older person.

3) Muscle mass: Lean muscle tissue burns more calories than fat tissue. Hence, athletes with larger muscle mass (such as bodybuilders) use more calories and have a higher BMR than athletes with smaller muscle mass (long distance runners, for example).

4) Weight: A heavier person (as long as she is not overweight) has a higher BMR than a lighter person.

5) Fat mass: Overweight persons, meanwhile, require less energy to maintain their body temperature than a normal

person, because of their insulating layer of fat. As a result, their BMR is lower than a person's of normal weight.

6) Temperature: Your BMR is higher on colder days in order to maintain your normal body temperature.

Work metabolism is defined as the energy consumed in the physical movements of work and sport. The work metabolism is added onto the basal metabolism, and the former depends on the length and difficulty of the activity. Hence, the total metabolism can be defined in the following equation:

Basal metabolism + work metabolism = total metabolism

The easiest way to see if your energy supply (as maintained by nutrition) corresponds to your energy demands is to weigh yourself on a regular basis. If more energy is taken in than is given off, you will gain weight. The energy nourishment of your food and the energy metabolism of your body are calculated in kilocalories. The energy nourishment of food is only a measurement for the assessment of optimal nutrition that a person can adapt to. Equally important is the proper interrelationship of the foods.

THE SIGNIFICANCE OF NUTRITION

Most people realize that a reasonable diet is a prerequisite for leading a healthy and productive life. Nonetheless, people who possess an extensive knowledge of nutrition do not always eat properly. Why? One reason may be the difficulty of changing long-established eating habits. The persuasiveness of commercials and the biased explanations of the so-called "health fanatics," which leave the general population with unanswered questions concerning nutrition, may also be partly responsible for unhealthy eating habits.

BASIC RULES FOR FOLLOWING A NUTRITIOUS DIET

It is not that difficult to eat nutritiously. With the help of a food wheel (see illustration), you can easily put together a nutritious diet. This wheel was developed by the Red Cross and divides foods into groups according to the kind of nutrients they contain. It differs from the basic four food groups in that fruits and vegetables are placed in separate groups, and it distinguishes whole-grain products from enriched products.

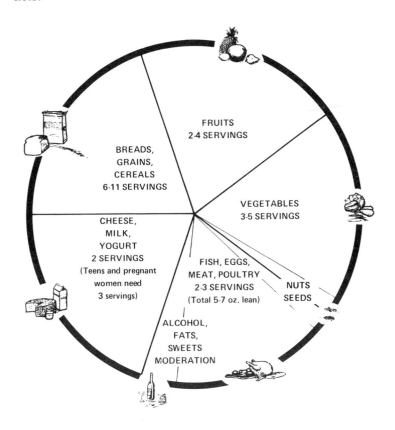

Whole-grain and enriched products (such as breads and cereals) provide carbohydrates, roughage and vitamin B, which plays an important role in the breakdown of carbohydrates. The basic grains include wheat, rice, corn and oats. Of the four, oats contain the most protein.

Fruits and vegetables provide mostly vitamins and minerals, but they also absorb carbohydrates easily. Potatoes (a

starch) are a better source of energy than rice or noodles because they have more carbohydrates, as well as more potassium, magnesium, calcium, phosphorous and iron. Com-
bined with rice, corn, grains or sesame seeds, legumes are an
excellent vegetable source of protein and include soybeans,
peanuts, black-eyed peas, kidney beans, chickpeas, navy
beans, pinto beans and lima beans.

Milk products are in another group, and include cheese
and yogurt. They are excellent buys for high-quality protein
(as are the legumes in the vegetable group), and above all,
the best source of calcium. One eight-ounce glass of milk
provides eight grams of protein, about one-sixth to one-
eighth of an adult's daily requirement.

Animal foodstuffs—meat, fish, poultry and eggs—make
up another group. These foods provide animal protein and
important vitamins and minerals such as iron. However,
they also provide considerable quantities of fats and cholesterol. Excessive consumption of red meat and eggs can result
in elevated serum cholesterol levels. Thus, you should try to
limit your intake of these foods since high serum cholesterol
levels increase the risk of heart disease. In principle, you can
maintain a nutritious diet without the animal foodstuffs, assuming that you obtain sufficient quantities of the essential
nutrients from the other groups, especially high-quality protein, vitamin B and iron. A diet of only legumes, grains,
fruits, vegetables and milk products is known as a lactovege-
tarian diet. Many long distance runners are lactovegetarians.

COMBINATION OF MEALS

Not only the nutritional value of foods, but their cost and
your taste will determine your diet. Proper nutrition has its
price, but that doesn't mean you must pay exorbitantly for it.
If you begin your day with foods like milk, yogurt or cheese,
and supplement them with fresh fruits and vegetables in
season, you will already have a reasonably well-balanced
diet. If you also regularly run and use little sugar, fat and alcohol in preparing your meals, your health will not suffer
from an occasional slice of cake or an alcoholic drink. The fact

that excess sugar in your diet contributes to many diseases does not mean that every teaspoon of sugar is dangerous. Paracelsus's soften-quoted saying applies here also: "The quantity of a substance determines its degree of harmfulness."

Replacing refined sugar with honey, however, doesn't solve the problem of excessive sugar. If your daily sugar consumption exceeds 110 grams, replacing refined sugars with honey will probably not prevent the same nutritional problems (excessive intake of calories, tooth decay and hypoglycemia). Although honey does contain minerals—mostly potassium, calcium and phosphorus—these nutrients are present in such minute quantities that they are an insignificant contribution to your diet.

BEVERAGES FROM A NUTRITIONAL PERSPECTIVE

Fruit juices represent a sensible supplement to your diet. Their nutritional value is based on their vitamins, minerals, trace elements and water. Children especially need to drink healthy beverages. If you consider that on a hot day young people can easily drink two liters of sugared drinks, it is not surprising how drinks can have a detrimental effect on a young person's nutrition. The sugar contained in that amount of soft drink satisfies half of the energy needs of a child, yet provides none of the essential nutrients.

Nutritional problems are often the result of improper intake of fluids. Our drinks often contain excessive amounts of sugar. The increased demand for proper nutrition in the past few years has led to a growing use of fruit juices and soft drinks. The only problem is that even individuals who are nutrition-conscious are sometimes unaware of the contents of their drinks. Is it fruit juice or just colored sugar water? Fruit juices and fruit drinks are shelved together in the stores. Although these completely different drinks are easy to distinguish by their names, their qualitative differences are known by relatively few people.

Fruit juice is liquified fruit, and is 100 percent juice made up of one or more kinds of fruit (freshly squeezed or frozen concentrate). Fruit drinks, though, are not 100 percent juice.

Rather, they are a mixture of juice, water, sugar, and possibly artificial coloring and preservatives. If any sugar is added to juice, the manufacturer is required to list sugar as one of the ingredients on the product's label. You can distinguish concentrated juice from fresh-squeezed juice by the required notice "made from concentrate" found on the label.

The U.S. Food and Drug Administration has specific regulations concerning juices and fruit drinks. FDA regulations state that some pulp from the initial extraction of juice can be added to a product, and sold as fruit juice or concentrated fruit juice. The excess pulp is not thrown away, but is often sold to companies that make other kinds of beverages, including fruit drinks. The name "fruit drink" and the colorful fruits that are on the drink's label are deceiving: There is actually much less fruit in the drinks than the consumer is led to believe. If you take into account how diluted the drinks are, and how much sugar they contain, a label depicting a water faucet with a bag of sugar would be closer to the truth. As long as such misleading advertising exists, we can only advise you to look carefully before buying fruit juice. You shouldn't only look at the labels, but actually read the list of ingredients carefully, especially the ones in fine print.

Because of their high sugar content, soft drinks will quench your thirst for only short periods of time. Indeed, as thirst quenchers and replenishers of fluids, fruit juices and lemonade, too, are unsuitable after a sweaty workout, since their ability to quench your thirst and refresh you decrease with increasing amounts of fruit in the juice. Better thirst quenchers are mineral water mixed with fruit juice, sweetened lemon juice or tea with lemon juice and sweetener.

DRINKING AND RUNNING

All runners sweat and, hence, lose body fluids to varying degrees. If you lose water to the environment without replenishing it in some way, you incur what is known as "negative water balance." In the December 1984 issue of *Runner's World*, Joe Henderson discussed the 1984 Olympic marathon. He pointed out that Alberto Salazar lost 17 pounds due to sweating, according to Athletics West exercise physiologist

Jack Daniels, M.D. During the race Salazar drank back only five pounds of that weight, translating to a net liquid loss of a gallon and a half.

In the April 1982 issue of *Runner's World*, Richard Pearce, Ph.D., discussed the vital role fluids play in running. Pearce noted that long distance runners lose from one to six liters of water when running. He later referred to research being conducted by Dr. David Costill, director of the Human Performance Laboratory at Ball State University in Muncie, Ind. Costill has studied Olympic marathoners during training workouts, but his results provide important information for novice runners as well. He examined the water needs of runners before, during and after runs. By comparing runners who received water with those who ran without any replenishment, he showed that it is important for runners to drink liquids during and after a race to replace lost body fluid. In addition, drinking liquids lowers the body temperature. Costill recalled a middle-aged man who collapsed during a 10-K with a rectal temperature of 109 degrees.

What drink is best suited for replenishing this lost fluid? As a thirst quencher, water ranks as the ideal drink. Other acceptable prerace drinks are skim milk, lemonade, clear beef or chicken broth, bouillon or consomme. The so-called "thirst quenchers" are designed to replace the water and electrolytes the body loses through sweat. Unfortunately, most of these drinks contain high concentrations of salt, requiring the stomach to dilute them, resulting in an initial loss of body water. These electrolyte replacements are, in the words of one sports-health specialist, "useless."

Yet doesn't the body need those lost electrolytes? Unquestionably, but they can be obtained elsewhere. Dr. Patricia Beckworth of Children's Hospital in Los Angeles says that we can easily replace these lost electrolytes through the foods we eat. Costill concurs, stating that there is "no evidence in runners that there is any occasion where potassium (which helps regulate water balance) or other salt unbalance develops [provided that] a person eats a good, normal diet."

ORGANIZATION OF MEALS

The number and size of meals influence our fitness. Instead of eating three large meals, it is more sensible to eat more small meals throughout the day. Smaller, more frequent meals place less stress on the digestive system. Experiments have also shown that persons eating three large meals per day will gain weight more easily than persons who eat several smaller meals. Certain metabolic processes are responsible for this. If too much food is eaten at one time, the body cannot digest all of the nutrients immediately, and a portion of them will be stored as fatty deposits.

Every person has different nutritional requirements. If family members don't eat sufficient amounts of certain foods at mealtime, it is easy for them to make up these differences in the form of snacks. These snacks should include foods such as milk, yogurt, vegetable juice and fruit. It is not that difficult to follow these recommendations, if you know which nutrients are found in which foods.

Protein: The most important sources of animal protein are meat, fish, eggs and dairy products. Sources of vegetable protein are bread, nuts, grain products, soy products and legumes. Protein serves primarily as the building block for cells and tissues and for the formation of hormones, enzymes, antibodies and hemoglobin. Intensive endurance exercises increase the activity of these substances.

There are both "complete" and "incomplete" proteins. Most animal proteins fall into the former category because they contain adequate amounts of the eight essential amino acids and some of the nonessential ones as well. Foods such as meat, fish, poultry and dairy products, then, will satisfy the body's protein requirements. Incomplete proteins are obtained from vegetables sources, and lack sufficient quantities of one or more of the essential amino acids. As a result, if you eat peanut butter alone, you will lack the amino acid methionine. But if you spread that peanut butter on a slice of wheat bread, which lacks sufficient quantities of the amino acids lysine and isoleucine, but has plenty of methionine, you will have a complete protein. Peanut butter and wheat are called complementary proteins; together, they form a complete protein. The chart that follows is a list of such complementary proteins and suggests ways you can combine vegetable sources of protein to satisfy your body's protein needs.

VEGETABLE PROTEINS

If you combine vegetable proteins in the same meal in any of the ways suggested below, you will obtain complete protein equivalent to the protein in meat and other animal foods.

Rice with	Wheat
	Legumes*
	Sesame seeds
Wheat with	Legumes*
	Soybeans and peanuts
	Soybeans and sesame seeds
	Rice and soybeans
Legumes* with	Corn
	Rice
	Wheat
	Sesame seeds
	Barley
	Oats

*Appropriate legumes include soybeans, peanuts, black-eyed peas, kidney beans, chickpeas, navy beans, pinto beans, and lima beans.

Hemoglobin, which is made up almost entirely of protein, is vital to the health of the athlete because it transports the oxygen from the lungs to the cells. While at rest, a person uses 300 milliliters of oxygen per minute for breathing. With intensive exercise, oxygen consumption can increase to as much as six liters per minute. To maintain an intensive training program these days, it is no longer possible to work out with the generally accepted level of protein intake—about 0.15 ounces per ten pounds of body weight. Protein deficiency results in weakened performance capability long before health problems arise. How much is enough?

Fat: Besides the visible cooking and spreading fats—butter, margarine and oil—many foods contain hidden amounts of fat. Sausage, cheese, nuts, baked goods, chocolate products and mayonnaise all possess notable quantities of fat. You can reduce your intake of fat by eating lean meat and poultry, low-fat cheeses and reducing the amount of fat you cook with. A diet rich in fats robs the muscles of needed glycogen and weakens your endurance.

The classification of carbohydrates

Types of carbohydrates	Included in this group	Contained in these food sources
monosaccharides (simple sugars)	glucose fruit sugar	fruit, honey fruit, honey
disaccharides (double sugars)	cane and beet sugar	table sugar sweets
	malt sugar milk sugar	beer milk, yogurt
oligosaccharides (complex sugars)	sugar mixtures food concentrates	maltose (corn starch)
polysaccharides (multiple sugars)	starch noodles, whole grain cereals	potatoes, rice, bread
	glycogen	liver
	dextrin	zwieback
	cellulose	plants

THE EFFECT OF CARBOHYDRATES ON YOUR PERFORMANCE

The human body can store carbohydrates in the form of glycogen deposits in only limited quantities in the muscles and liver. Complex carbohydrates from grain products, potatoes, rice and noodles are preferred, since they are absorbed, and hence depleted, more slowly. As a result, these foods deliver energy continuously after they are eaten. Women runners with long, daily workouts should make sure they include plenty of carbohydrates in their diet. Although the glycogen supply will be depleted after a workout, you can replenish it within twenty-four hours by maintaining a high-carbohydrate diet. Normally, the process would take up to three days. If your glycogen supply is low, you can complete your workouts at only a low intensity level. The ability to maintain a certain pace over longer distances depends on the size of the runner's glycogen supply.

We have known for many years that carbohydrates can improve endurance. Even 2000 years ago, Roman soldiers ate porridge rich in carbohydrates to improve their daily endurance. There are many theories as to what makes up an effective high-carbohydrate diet; many of these diets are unrealistic in attempting to produce the greatest possible efficiency in workouts. Pizzas and noodle dishes that are eaten the night before most marathons—during the so-called carbo-loading parties—are really richer in fat than they are in carbohydrates. The recommended diet for distance runners consists of 60 percent carbohydrate, 12 to 15 percent protein and 25 to 28 percent fat. With our normal eating habits, it is not easy to maintain a diet that consists of 60 percent carbohydrates.

Because of people's high consumption of fat (40 percent), our current intake of carbohydrates consists of only 40 percent of the entire diet. Nutritional scientists, who in West Germany recommend carbohydrate intake levels of 50 to 55 percent, and in the United States recommend 58 percent, clearly agree with distance runners that diets should include more carbohydrates.

VITAMINS, MINERALS AND TRACE ELEMENTS

These nutrients have a greater influence on the completion of many life processes than is often realized. A shortage of certain nutrients depletes your physical resources and weakens your resistance to colds and infections. The most common shortage is an iron deficiency. Almost one of every two women who has not yet gone through menopause may suffer from this deficiency. In view of the role that iron plays in the transport of oxygen and the concomitant increase in iron use, female distance runners have greater iron requirements than nonrunners. This greater requirement of iron is explained by increased oxygen needs and a corresponding increase in the blood cells used to transport the oxygen. (More red blood cells mean more hemoglobin, hence more iron in the whole blood.)

Women need more iron during pregnancy, lactation and menstruation. During the menstrual cycle alone, women need almost twice the iron that men do. It's not surprising, then, that about 5 percent of American women have mild iron-deficiency anemia (when your blood is not tired, but *you* are). This kind of anemia is the nation's most common nutritional deficiency. An iron deficiency in a pregnant woman can lead to premature birth.

You can easily develop an iron deficiency from a decrease in iron absorption from your foods. For example, if you consume eggs or tea at the same meal as vegetable-derived iron, absorption of the iron will be limited. Losses of blood may also deplete the body's iron stores. Hence, women who menstruate heavily or are frequent blood donors may also need more iron. In both of these cases, iron supplements can eliminate the deficiencies. An iron deficiency may develop in strict vegetarians, who obtain all of their iron from vegetable sources; in dieters who sharply reduce their caloric intake; and in persons who eat foods that are high in fats, sugar and calories but low in nutrients.

Sources of iron include meat, rolled oats, wheat germ, whole grain products, legumes and potatoes. You should be aware, though, that the body cannot absorb the iron in all of these foods equally. For example, while 20 to 30 percent of the iron from meat will be absorbed, only 1 to 5 percent of the iron from plants will be absorbed. Your absorption of iron will markedly improve if you eat foods rich in vitamin C, such as fruit, along with the iron-rich products.

Dr. Alois Mader of the Institute for Circulatory Research in West Germany determined that some world-class runners suffer from very low hemoglobin levels. Low levels of hemoglobin result in a lowered ability of the body to transport oxygen. A person suffering from this deficiency will transport less oxygen with every liter of blood. This lowered level of hemoglobin limits how much blood the heart can pump, a problem compounded by the fact that under exertion, the heart is already working harder. Thus, a decreasing hemoglobin level will lower the maximum oxygen uptake and fitness level of the runner.

Therefore, Dr. Mader advises all women who run intensively more than an hour daily or more than once per week to regularly monitor their hemoglobin levels. This level should not drop below thirteen grams per deciliter, ideally remaining between 13.5 to 14.5 g/dl or higher. If your hemoglobin level drops below 12.5 g/dl, you should allow a doctor to examine your blood. Before an important workout or race Dr. Mader recommends that runners take low dosages of iron-vitamin preparations as a preventive measure against iron deficiency. The proper range would be fifty to sixty milligrams per tablet. For best results, you can alternate three- or four-week periods of taking the iron supplements with longer periods of taking no supplements. Any iron deficiency that suddenly appears could then be quickly remedied, allowing the runner to avoid any setbacks in either her running or overall health.

Another nutritional problem for running women is athletic amenorrhea, the absence or suppression of menstruation. This condition, which afflicts women who train intensively, was originally believed to prevent conception, since the mothers would not have enough body fat to nourish an unborn baby. Barney Sanborn and Wiltz Wagner, exercise physiologists at the University of Colorado, debunked this theory after measuring the body fat of fourteen women who ran at least forty miles per week. Half the group menstruated while the other half didn't, but the two groups had the same amount of body fat. Susan Brooks, a colleague of Sanborn's, took the experiment one step farther. She analyzed the diets of these young women, and found out that the amenorrheic runners were very weight-conscious and ate sporadically throughout the day. In addition, they ate very little meat, although they obtained sufficient protein from other sources. Brooks believes that the women's low meat consumption and irregular eating patterns may have influenced their reproductive hormones, resulting in the amenorrhea. More tests on this subject are bound to unlock the relationship between meals, meat and menstruation.

PROPER PREPARATION OF FOOD PREVENTS THE LOSS OF NUTRIENTS

Just as important as choosing the correct food is the proper storage and careful preparation of meals. Many nutrients are sensitive to light, air and heat. What should you be aware of? In preparing foods, especially fresh fruit, vegetables and potatoes, the following rules are worth observing:

1) When peeling and cleaning foods, remove only as much as you have to.
2) Wash foods quickly but thoroughly.
3) Do not chop foods smaller than necessary.
4) Cook foods over low flame whenever possible.
5) Don't overcook the foods.
6) Don't keep cooked foods warm too long.
7) Refrigerate leftovers until they are to be reused.

EATING BEFORE A RUN

The saying "You cannot study on a full stomach" can also be applied to running. But it is not advisable to run on an empty stomach either. Basically, you should eat your last meal two or three hours before you run. If you suffer hunger pangs half an hour to an hour before the run, have drinks rich in carbohydrates or easily digestible food, neither of which should interfere with your run.

The following is a recipe for a drink rich in carbohydrates: Mix one glass of fruit juice or low-fat milk with two teaspoons of instant rolled oats. (Instant rolled oats are practical and provide an adequate source of carbohydrate in an easily absorbable form.) Examples of easily digested foods rich in carbohydrates:

1) Fruit: bananas, oranges or peeled apples (one-half to three-quarters of a pound).
2) Mashed potatoes, rice or noodles prepared with little fat.
3) One slice of crispbread with apple sauce.
4) One cup of low-fat vegetable or meat bouillon with added ingredients.
5) One portion of porridge.
6) Dried fruit: fruit slices without nuts, dried prunes or apricots (about a quarter pound).

It is important to eat these foods slowly and chew thoroughly. Chewing well will make the foods easier to digest.

A study completed at Ball State University in Muncie, Indiana, suggests that eating a sugar may help your performance. Exercise physiologists David Costill and Mark Hargreaves reported in the *Journal of Medicine and Science in Sports and Exercise* that in two separate tests, subjects bicycled with and without a sweetened food (175 sugar calories). In the test with sweetened food, the subjects burned only about two-thirds the amount of glycogen than in the test without the sweetened food. In addition, during the ride's final sprint, the bicyclists were able to pedal 45 percent longer when they ate the sweetened food. The consumed food appears to slow the depletion of the stores of glycogen, the substance runners try to build up through carbo-loading.

NUTRITION BEFORE A MARATHON

Any first-time marathoner has legitimate fears about "hitting the wall," an expression used to describe the exhaustion that can force a runner to either drop out or walk during a longer race. A well-known method of preventing this kind of exhaustion is carbo-loading, in which the runner actually increases the stores of glycogen in the body (carbohydrates are stored in the body as glycogen). Current research suggests that a steady high carbohydrate diet is better than carbo-loading for a specific race. Maintaining a diet high in carbo-hydrates prevents you from wearing down your glycogen supply during training. Eat these foods every day: whole grains (breads, pastas, cereals and rice), vegetables (pota-toes, corn, beans and peas) and fruits.

Many runners, though, still swear by the pre-race carbo-loading that often culminates in a carbo-loading party featur-ing foods such as spaghetti or pizza. To carbo-load in prepa-ration for an important race: Complete your last intensive training three or four days before the competition, thereby depleting your glycogen supply in the muscles. You should follow up this depletion with meals heavy in complex carbo-hydrates (starches) up to the day of the competition. A carbo-hydrate-rich diet after intensive training can provide your leg muscles with an excess of stored glycogen. The glycogen supply is not just filled to its previous level, but is actually increased. This increase of your glycogen supply is labeled "super compensation."

Glycogen binds itself to potassium. Consequently, during the time you eat foods rich in carbohydrates, you should also eat large quantities of potassium. Foods rich in potassium are fruit (fresh and dried), vegetables and grain products.

Many runners find this depletion and loading of carbohy-drates wearing, both physically and psychologically. In any case, you should first try this nutritional method either in training or before a less important competition, as people's digestive systems vary in their reaction to this kind of diet. After taking a carbohydrate concentrate, I myself suffered such bad stomach pain that I had to walk the first portion of a fun-run. Other runners who took the same concentrate had no problems whatsoever.

I believe that a modified carbohydrate diet, less extreme than the second mentioned diet, will cause fewer problems. In this modified version, you also train intensively six days before a competition to deplete your glycogen supply. The first three days you should eat foods low in carbohydrate (but not lacking them completely), including complex carbohy-drates, such as potatoes, bread or whole-grain cereals. Leading up to the competition, you should then eat a carbohydrate-rich diet.

A well-rounded diet, as depicted by the food wheel, is of utmost importance. It should be both rich in carbohydrates and low in fat, contain sufficient protein and include your daily requirements of minerals, trace elements and vitamins. Since the marathon is an unusually strenuous activity, you may want to take special measures regarding your diet to maximize your sports performance. A carefully conceived nutritional plan can increase your overall fitness level.

ELEVEN: WEIGHT LOSS THROUGH RUNNING

Obesity has been a major problem in the United States for many decades. The National Center for Health Statistics completed a survey on 13,000 Americans aged eighteen to seventy-four in the early 1970s. The survey showed that adult American men and women are anywhere from fifteen to thirty pounds overweight. Worse still, scientists believe that so-called normal weight—which was used to calculate the above statistics—is 10 percent too high.

How has this problem evolved? With increasing modernization, Americans face fewer physical demands on a day-to-day basis. To get enough exercise, people have to "create" it in the form of sports such as running. Our high-fat diet must also take some of the responsibility for the obesity problem.

Metabolism plays the decisive role in weight loss. When the body takes in more energy than it can burn off, you gain weight. This process is influenced by many factors, especially the basal metabolism and work metabolism. In fact, there is a direct correlation between exercise and the body's metabolic rate. In a study completed at the University of California, participants performed strenuous physical exercise in order to measure any changes in their metabolic rates. A full *four hours* after the activity, the participants' metabolic rates were 7.5 to 28 percent higher than when they hadn't exercised.

There are only two methods of losing weight over a long period of time: limiting your intake of food or increasing your metabolism. The most effective means of losing weight is by combining these two methods: adopting a well-planned diet and a specific sports program.

Of all the endurance sports, running will burn up the most energy. Running at an average pace of ten minutes per mile, the body burns up more than 660 calories per hour. By comparison, bicycling burns up considerably less energy. To work off the energy contained in a bar of chocolate, for example, a person would have to bicycle about eighty minutes, yet would only have to run for forty-five minutes.

When burning off calories while running, not only are your pace, effort, fitness level and the air temperature important, but also your bodyweight. That is, an overweight person uses more energy than a person with ideal weight if the two persons run at the same pace and have the same training background. In contrast, the metabolic rate during cycling is little influenced by the weight of the cyclist.

Sports are an important part of a weight-loss program, not only by speeding up the metabolism, but also as a means of curbing your appetite. By participating in sports on a regular basis, you normalize the natural stimulus to eat, which is improperly adjusted in many people. We can distinguish between "internally-cued" and "externally-cued" persons. The former eat when their brains signal physical hunger—when the body needs more fuel to function. Externally-cued people, however, eat in response to cues from their environment. These persons eat when offered food, when they see a picture of a tasty snack or to soothe themselves during times of stress.

It is clear, then, that the consumption of food should not be viewed merely as a physiological process, but also as a psychological one. Eating is of varying importance to people. For some, food functions as an apparent problem solver or as a release from boredom and worries, for others a kind of replacement for something missing from their lives, such as job satisfaction or a satisfying relationship.

Most weight-loss programs do not consider these psychological factors, and consequently, these programs usually succeed only for short periods, and do not provide the desired long-term success most people seek. Yet these factors play a major role in weight control. Therefore, every weight-loss program should suggest how you can understand and control your eating habits.

A successful diet requires direction and advice—ideally in a group situation—because the initial weight loss leads to greater success when you aren't alone. By sharing your problems with a group, it is easier to endure the diet, motivate yourself, receive reinforcement and accept criticism.

Mrs. Christel Stumpf of West Germany was thirty-nine years old, five-feet, six-inches tall and weighed 175 pounds when she went on her first run. She didn't have the support of a group, although she would have preferred running with others. Despite this handicap, she not only lost weight but enjoyed psychological benefits from employing a diet and exercise program.

Christel started with fifty-yard runs. She had a weak heart and varicose veins. But by persevering until she could increase her runs to four miles, she found she had not only lost weight, but that she had strengthened her heart, lost her varicose veins, and even had more energy at work. Eight years later, her friends tell her she looks younger than when she started running. She now depends on running for her well-being. "I would feel incomplete without it," she says. "Since I started running, my life has been greatly enriched. I will certainly not stop."

Mrs. Stumpf occasionally participates in fun-runs and even marathons. After four years of training, she ran her fastest marathon in three and a half hours. Her favorite run is a seventeen-mile loop around Lake Wolfgang. To maintain her body weight of 142 pounds, Mrs. Stumpf must run regularly. If she is forced to curb her weekly mileage (because of a shortage of time), she will immediately gain weight. Not only does she feel most comfortable at her current weight, but she is also the most efficient.

SO-CALLED IDEAL WEIGHT—THE NIGHTMARE OF ALL OVERWEIGHT PERSONS

It is simple to determine your exact weight, but difficult to calculate your ideal weight. Which criteria or formulas should you use? There are presently about fifteen different methods of figuring a person's optimal weight, yet none of the results will agree with one another. I will discuss three methods of calculating ideal weight.

The easiest formula to work by hand is the Broca formula, created by a French anthropologist and surgeon of that name (1824-1880). The Broca formula, applicable only to adults, is calculated with a person's height: Height in centimeters - 100 = bodyweight in kilograms (Broca's normal weight).

This formula is insufficient for individual standards, because it does not take into account the differences in body build and composition. Hence, it can't be used for either very tall or very short persons. My average bodyweight is about 134 pounds. According to the Broca formula, I am about six pounds overweight.

Interesting enough, this ideal weight corresponds almost exactly with the figures from the table that follows, taken from the Pacific Mutual Life Insurance Company. They were derived from a study by the life-insurance industry of the impact of weight on mortality.

IDEAL WEIGHT IN POUNDS

			Age		
Height	*20-29*	*30-39*	*40-49*	*50-59*	*60-69*
			Men		
5'3"	125	129	130	131	130
5'6"	135	140	142	143	142
5'9"	149	153	155	156	155
6'0"	161	166	167	168	167
6'3"	176	181	183	184	180
			Women		
4'10"	97	102	106	109	111
5'1"	106	109	114	118	120
5'4"	114	118	122	127	129
5'7"	123	127	132	137	140
5'10"	134	138	142	146	147

Measuring your body fat, as is often done in laboratories, can be a more reliable method of determining your ideal body weight than tables or mathematical formulas. Fat is stored in the subcutis. As a result, it is possible to measure excess weight in the layers of fat there. From this measurement of body fat, it can be determined whether the body weight is high due to large fat deposits or muscle mass. There are two ways of measuring that fat: by pinching the fat with calipers and by submerging the subject in water. The second way is the most accurate body-fat measurement.

None of these methods, however, may be able to give you your ideal weight. National-class runner Heidi Hutterer stands five-feet, three-inches tall and weighs between 87 and 89 pounds. All methods of calculating ideal weight would certainly classify Hutterer as being underweight. Erich Vellage, her coach, and Dr. Mader, a sportsmedicine consultant for a sports college in Cologne, both agree that she weighs too little. Yet Hutterer feels that her best competitive weight is eighty-eight pounds. She states: "When I weigh ninety pounds, I feel heavy and cannot run as well. If my weight drops to eighty-six pounds, I feel fine, though on runs of eighteen miles or longer, I often get hunger pangs and really cannot finish the run. I feel strongest when my weight remains at eighty-eight pounds. At this weight I can also produce my best performances."

In summary, obesity is the result of the body taking in more calories than it burns off. The easiest and most efficient method of losing weight is by combining a program of a well-conceived diet and a specific sports activity. Starting some form of physical activity is important physiologically for two reasons. First, it will speed up your metabolism and your body will burn off calories more rapidly. Second, participating in a sport such as running will normalize your natural impulse to eat. Most weight-loss programs view overeating only as a physiological process, and neglect the psychological dynamics of the problem. A program that addresses both the physiological and psychological aspects of weight control will probably achieve the greatest success.

TWELVE:
SMOKING
AND ALCOHOL

While obesity is the most serious nutritional problem in the United States, the surgeon general stated in 1982 that smoking is the main preventable cause of death in our society, and *the most important* public health issue.

How do women fit into this picture? One of the most lucrative markets for cigarettes is young women. Parallel to this rise among young female smokers has been an increase in smoking-related diseases such as lung cancer, bronchitis and coronary heart disease. While earlier it was quite rare for a woman of child-bearing age to suffer from coronary thrombosis, this disease is not uncommon today among women smokers. Nine out of ten women with thrombosis are heavy smokers. Besides these typical smoking-related diseases, there is an additional risk for women: miscarriage. In the first three months of pregnancy, women who smoke are two times more likely to miscarry than nonsmoking women. In addition, the number of premature deliveries among heavy smokers is two to three times higher than that of nonsmokers. A related statistic is that the children of women smokers must be hospitalized on account of respiratory problems two to three times as often in their first year of life as the children of nonsmoking mothers.

Although most women try to stop or limit their smoking, only a few are successful. Most prefer to accept their lack of willpower rather than abstain from cigarettes. Friends and family members who smoke wield a great deal of influence in creating the smoker's habit. Heavy smokers often note that they had role models who smoked.

The smoker's desire for cigarettes is primarily the result of an addiction to nicotine. In small quantities, nicotine stimulates activity in the brain, and in the process can temporarily relieve fatigue and listlessness. For the smoker to feel the same degree of stimulation, she unconsciously will smoke to maintain the same level of nicotine. Hence, she will always smoke when the nicotine level drops off. If the smoker changes over to low-tar cigarettes, she will inevitably smoke more of them in order to maintain the same level of nicotine. Consequently, the advantages of low-tar, filter-tipped cigarettes are negated: the filters simply force the smoker to smoke more cigarettes to make up for the nicotine trapped by the filters.

The no-smoking movement in the United States is strengthening, resulting in a shifting of attitudes on smoking. A major impetus of this attitude shift is evidence that nonsmokers exposed to a smoking environment (at work, home or in public places such as restaurants or bars) are seriously affected by the smoke. James Repace, a policy analyst with the Environmental Protection Agency, has calculated that if a person works in an office with a typical number of smokers, she breathes in the equivalent of three low-tar cigarettes per day, increasing her risk of cancer by *three times* (*Runner's World*, September 1984).

Repace and Alfred H. Lowrey, a research chemist at the Naval Research Laboratory, published a paper in May 1980 in *Science* that stated that the amount of indoor pollution created by smoking is greater than the air pollution on a crowded Los Angeles freeway. The paper concludes, "Clearly, indoor air pollution from tobacco smoke presents a serious risk to the health of nonsmokers."

Rolf Schippers, with a background in psychology, went through a program designed to help people kick their nicotine habits. He participated in the program to understand why women smoke. He concluded: "In order to explain this phenomenon, you should examine the changes in sex roles that have taken place in our society during the past two generations. There are many jobs, previously dominated by men, that are now open to women as well. The feminist movement has paved the way for more women in the work place. In the same fashion, the development of women's smoking has also been accelerated by the feminist movement. There are few social pressures that discourage young women from smoking."

The story of Ursula Schaefer, a runner and an ex-smoker, shows how running can assist women in kicking the cigarette habit. At age twenty-eight, she began jogging after enjoying a fun-run that a fellow employee challenged her to participate in. She increased her distance, realizing women were ideally suited for running. She hadn't quit smoking, though, but then decided to curb her habit when she found herself coughing during her runs.

Despite cutting down, she was still addicted to the three cigarettes she allowed herself each day. Finally, shame and a haunting image of a smoker's black lungs she saw in a biology class gave her sufficient motivation to stop completely.

The first six weeks were difficult. Physically, she suffered terrible shakes and an underfunctioning thyroid gland. Psychologically, she became irritable, and sought people with whom she could argue. She says that, "Running was my only outlet, which I did extensively and with pleasure," and now happily reports that, "Today I am 'clean' and am starting to lose the eleven pounds of weight that I gained as a result of a eating binge. Every attempt I made to stop smoking was followed by a period of overeating."

Mrs. Schaefer's weight gain after stopping smoking is typical and is not simply due to her desire to put something in the mouth other than a cigarette. Smoking increased the production of Mrs. Schaefer's thyroid gland, as well as her basal metabolism. This rise in her basal metabolism led to a need for more energy-supplying food.

In addition, smoking can suppress feelings of hunger. After stopping smoking, you can probably curb the initial desire to put something in your mouth by chewing gum. Some ex-smoking runners gain satisfaction by eating licorice.

Smoking is a difficult habit to break. But along with an awareness of the physiological and psychological responses encountered as you kick the habit, running can help you liberate yourself from this dangerous obstacle to a healthy life.

WOMEN AND ALCOHOL

While smoking has developed a negative image in the past few years, alcohol consumption has become more socially acceptable. It has even become a status symbol. A well-stocked bar or wine cellar can be as impressive as a Mercedes Benz. There are many reasons for drinking: habit, loneliness, boredom and even social pressure. Since alcohol has become such an accepted part of our lives, there is the pressure to conform, as when someone pushes a drink into your hand at a party. People drink to hide fears and inhibitions, or to relax. Men and women alike enjoy a before-dinner drink to wind down.

The social pressure to drink is fueled by subtle advertising. The typical beer commercial, for example, depicts a crowd of people—often at a party or in a bar—drinking and having a great time. The message is clear: drink our product and your life will be as fun-filled as the lives of the people in the commercial.

These products are described in such attractive terms as "affordable," "full-bodied," "exquisite," "pure" and so on. A typical slogan for beer is "Brewed where tradition and nature are still unspoiled." Such slogans are written carefully to appeal to the values of the viewer. The concepts of tradition and nature are designed to create images of a drink that is healthy (following the example of "natural" foods) and has stood the test of time. Wine commercials often show an elderly "connoiseur" reverently describing the product's long-standing tradition. The viewer associates such an image with quality and, theoretically, goes out and buys the product.

THE EFFECTS OF ALCOHOL

Small quantities of alcohol are harmless to healthy people. It becomes dangerous when drinken in excess, leading to diseases of the internal organs or possibly to alcoholism. The

liver is the organ most easily damaged by drinking alcohol since it is here that alcohol is broken down.

How much alcohol is damaging depends on the sex and weight of the person. In general, women tolerate less alcohol than men. The manner in which the alcohol is drunk also plays a role in the effect it has on the body. If you quickly gulp down a couple of beers before dinner, the effect will likely be worse than if you calmly drink wine (the amount of alcohol being the same) with a meal. Drinking relatively small quantities of alcohol can cause health problems if you do not eat properly or if you possess an already damaged liver. For persons already dependent on alcohol, even limited amounts of the drug are a health hazard.

Assuming that you are in good health, will moderate drinking affect your training? This question was answered by Dave Lightsey, M.S., in *Runner's World*'s August 1983 issue. Lightsey suggests that runners abstain before, during and after a race. He states, "Alcohol does not provide caloric food value equivalent to carbohydrates. On the contrary, when alcohol is ingested a significant increase in energy is required to metabolize it. This additional energy requirement not only depletes your energy reserves, but also puts an additional strain on your body's ability to maintain proper temperature." Lightsey adds that drinking excessively puts a strain on the liver, and that the ingested alcohol accounts for 70 percent of the liver's total oxygen uptake. This added workload interferes with the organ's normal functions, such as removing waste products from the bloodstream, restoring depleted muscle and liver stores and eliminating toxic by-products of metabolism.

Beer is the alcoholic drink of preference for most runners. In the October 1983 issue of *Runner's World*, Dr. Melvin Williams addresses the benefits of this popular pre- and post-race drink. He notes that beer does contain nutrients—specifically, significant amounts of phosphorous, riboflavin, sodium, potassium and thiamine (more than 10 percent of the RDA). Yet these nutrients can be obtained from other food sources more efficiently. Williams quotes studies which show that alcohol does not affect performance in maximum endurance tests to exhaustion. In fact, alcohol may contribute to hypoglycemia (a deficiency of sugar in the blood) during prolonged exercise, as in a marathon. He adds that tests have not proved social drinking to be harmful before a race (as in a party the night before), *if the body fluids are replenished before race time.* Like coffee, alcohol is a diuretic, and may cause a loss of body fluids. A real danger related to that post-race beer may be the loss of psychomotor abilities. The old adage, "Don't drive if you drink," is worth remembering.

RUNNING AWAY FROM ALCOHOLISM

The transition from social drinking to alcoholism is a fluid one and often not foreseeable. Besides the habitual drinkers, the number of women who drink out of boredom or loneliness is large. Perhaps they drink because they would feel pain without it. To obtain that feeling of well-being, however, they need more and more alcohol. In this respect, alcohol is like all drugs. The addict who cannot break out of this vicious circle and remedy his or her difficulties by other means, inevitably destroys himself physically and spiritually.

Many women turn to running as a means of escaping their dependency on alcohol. Erika Werner of West Germany was one such woman. She lost her husband when she was forty-seven years old, and started to drink to relieve her grief. She explained the onset of and solution to her drinking problem: "After losing my husband, I could not imagine my world continuing in a normal fashion. Sundays were particularly difficult, since I had always spent them by the sports field with my husband, who played in a soccer league. I could not sleep at night, so I took a nightcap to fall asleep. That one drink suddenly became three or four. I decided that I had to seek out an activity on Sundays that was enjoyable and freed me from the dependency on alcohol.

"At that time, fun-runs were becoming popular. I thus began to jog twice a week in the forest, sometimes alone and sometimes with members of a gymnastics club. To take part in the fun-runs, I would need transportation. I subsequently got my driver's license and bought a small car. In May 1971, I drove to my first out-of-town fun-run. In my age division I finished third overall. The entire atmosphere of the fun-run was so enthralling that I participated in one again the very next weekend. From that point on, my running career took off. I gained so much pleasure from running; this exercise allowed me to become a happy person again. As of 1977 I had won more than 100 medals in competition. I won't give up running because first, it has given me peace of mind, and second, the workouts allow me to easily maintain my figure, without forsaking cake and chocolate."

In conclusion, women should view alcohol abuse as a serious problem. As shown by Erika Werner's story, heavy drinkers can break their dependency on alcohol by starting a sports activity such as running. Running can restore your sense of well-being and make weight-loss easier. Everyone can help erase the positive image that alcohol still carries with it. When entertaining guests, you should offer them nonalcoholic alternatives and avoid forcing alcohol on anyone. Women runners, meanwhile, can improve their performances by abstaining from alcohol before, during and after races. If you must drink, do so in moderation.

THIRTEEN: HOW RUNNING IMPROVES THE QUALITY OF LIFE

Why are more and more women starting to run? *Runner's World* sent out a questionnaire to women throughout the United States at the height of the running movement, asking them to respond to personal questions about the women's running scene. Surprisingly enough, the most predictable question, "Why do you run?" had the most provocative answers.

Here are some voices of women expressing heart to heart what running means to them, how they have grown, why they keep on going. The universality of their experiences creates a bridge of communication that women everywhere (runners and nonrunners) can relate to and learn from.

"Very honestly, I don't know exactly why I run. Probably the reasons are fundamentally very selfish: Running affords me some very private and very alert moments with myself. And for that hour, absolutely nobody counts as much as I do." *(Sofia Shafqat, Port Chester, New York)*

"The main thing seems to be my health. Since I started running two and a half years ago, I have had two head colds . . . both of which were minor. I used to get five or six colds a year. Now, if I feel bad, or think I may be getting a cold, I go for a long run, and literally, 'run it out of my system.' It works every time. Never have I gotten ill from running . . . Running has also helped eliminate the painful cramps I suffered almost every month during my period. I still get cramps from time to time, but none are ever severe enough to complain about. Also, I don't flow as heavily, and each period doesn't last a full seven days as it used to, but goes for about five—which is very pleasant for me." *(Elizabeth Guthrie, East Riverdale, Maryland)*

"I run because I enjoy the feeling the rest of the day. I'm much more energetic now than prior to my jogging days. I no longer have a tired feeling upon rising each day. My bladder and kidneys are better than they have been in years. (I don't have to go to the bathroom so frequently—my muscles are stronger now.) My weight is better distributed and my body is toned up. My resting heart rate ranges from fifty to sixty-four, but used to be somewhat higher, approximately sixty-eight to eighty-four. I'm not as irritable as I was, except when I find myself running too much. And food tastes really good on days when I run." *(Willie Ann Albea, Anniston, Alabama)*

"The main reason I run is because I like to win." *(Mary Spear, Winston-Salem, North Carolina)*

"It is difficult to put into words what running means to me. Some of my friends ridiculed me at first, and it was impossible for them to understand why I did it. Now they look at me and know why." *(Jean Cooper, Marietta, Georgia)*

"Why do I run? It has become a physical necessity and a mental balm. Physically I know I am in excellent shape; my resting pulse rate is 38 to 42; my cholesterol and triglycerides are low; my weight is lower than my high school weight, even though I must still watch what I eat . . . Running has given me more physical and mental energy. It has caused me to seek new goals in my middle years. Three and half years ago I went back to finish college. I was forty-one and had not been to school in twenty-one years. It was rather frightening, but my self-confidence has built through the last few years. I attribute a lot of that to running." *(Mary Anne McBrayer, Houston, Texas)*

"A man once told me he related to the 'sportsperson' in me. That nearly blew my mind. No one had ever said that before." *(Linda Palter, Washington, D.C.)*

"I run to break out of my shell—my conventional self. I put on shorts and a shirt in colors and styles I do not normally tolerate and run places I'm usually too self-conscious to walk through. Running is my alter ego." *(Pat Jennings, Oakland, California)*

"I would like to be a runner for the rest of my life. I have always enjoyed the outdoors, and running takes me there. I am an explorer and running helps orient me to my surroundings. I sleep better. And if I eat the wrong foods, it hurts my run. With running it's easier to avoid fattening foods." *(Carol Irvine, Upper Marlboro, Maryland)*

"I started running to escape from two small children and because my poor thirty-year-old body was in awful shape." *(Carolyn Sawyer, Pittsfield, Massachusetts)*

"Out in the woods, in view of the Hudson River, I feel very much at peace with myself and my environment." *(Cindy Piebes, Tarrytown, New York)*

"From running it is possible to feel part of America because you know that almost everyone runs." *(Jody Meier, Wilmington, Delaware)*

"I run because it makes me feel good—and it makes my dog feel good to get out and stretch his legs." *(Esther Sharp, Sumter, South Carolina)*

"I run because I feel beautiful when I run. My mind can go anywhere and be as calm or active as it wants ... while my body moves and stretches and reaches beyond." *(Jurate Kazickas, Washington, D.C.)*

"One of the most important reasons for running was to improve an asthma condition. I can't say that the asthma is cured, but it is under my control." *(Carol Yamate, Saratoga, California)*

"I run for the T-shirts and patches given to finishers." *(Audrey Dix, Washington, D.C.)*

"I quit smoking after twenty-two years ..." *(Nancy Baker, San Francisco, California)*

"I especially enjoy running along the beaches ... Kailua Beach ... on the windward side of Oahu, Hawaii. The sun sets brilliant orange and slowly the sea turns lavender and deep blue. It's exquisite!" *(Louise Teng, Boston, Massachusetts)*

"There is nothing static about running. My attitudes and expectations regarding running are constantly changing and are, to a good degree, cumulative." *(Mary A. Malmstedt, Dover, New Hampshire)*

"I started running out of desperation." *(Miriam Girard, Mountain View, California)*

"I run for a lot of reasons, but I think the main reason is that I'm addicted. I feel guilty and ashamed of myself when I don't run. When I run every day I seem to take pressure easier and I get more accomplished. Running doesn't waste time—it gives me more." *(Rosemarie Lagunas, Santa Clara, California)*

"Running is like meditating. Everyone ought to have an hour a day when they only think about their bodies, and their mind is relieved of petty everyday problems . . . I'm very competitive in my running, but not in my everyday life. I think this is partly because the successes I achieve while running races give me self-confidence, and I don't feel the need to prove myself so much in other areas . . . I think it is a basic human need to identify with some group or another. I love runners and enjoy their company, and it gives me a feeling of self-confidence to be identified as one. It is good to feel like I belong to a somewhat elite group." *(Katherine Austin, Darien, Connecticut)*

"Sound sleep—I tend to wake up in the morning without an alarm clock if I am running regularly." *(Carol Hall, Stanford, California)*

"Running has been good for my disposition. I didn't notice this myself, but my husband and my officemates have commented on the improvement. Others say I seem at peace with myself. I think I know why. I have never been good at anything athletic; I used to get Cs in gym and I don't play any sport. I'm no great runner, but I'm not a disaster. That's a neat feeling. In part, running makes me feel good about my body for the first time. I don't weigh less than I did before starting, but I'm slimmer and people notice it. For the first time I feel attractive and healthy." *(Susan Irving, Washington, D.C.)*

"I am a bright, creative free spirit who can get so buzzed up about an idea or project, I won't be able to sleep or I'll forget to eat. I try to project a positivism about my life and inject that in others. When I have problems or tensions or emotional blocks, running acts as a release and a purifier. It can be a great calming force and a great renewer. I run for the mental benefits. The physical ones have come along free of charge. I have toned up considerably and lost some weight; I do have more energy and sleep more soundly. I have more confidence and believe in myself more." *(Judith Kelly, Washington, D.C.)*

"Running relieves depression and it has eliminated my back problems." *(Marilyn Neveo, Ridgewood, New Jersey)*

"Running gives me increased confidence in tackling new problems. I also have fewer problems with constipation." *(Carol Swain, Albany, California)*

"I ran originally because at forty-four I needed exercise and was lazy, but I couldn't stand the sight of cellulite on my thighs so I tried running and hated it. I tried to do too much, had several fractures, shinsplints and Achilles tendinitis. But I noticed that when I did run I would always sleep better. I have Erbs paralysis and suffer from calcium deposits, arthritis and bursitis. Acupuncture was helping somewhat to relieve it, but this is costly treatment. I finally read an article in *The New York Times* written by a doctor who said that after the first twenty minutes, running produced the same affect as acupuncture. As soon as I mended I took to my Adidas again and instead of my half-mile jog I started running for half an hour, and it worked. My pains are dramatically reduced and I have actually gotten to love running. I listen to my body only." *(Mary Ann Taylor, Boston, Massachusetts)*

"I run because it's something I feel compelled to do—not as a task but as an inner drive ... I like the challenge of a steep hill and the sound of my breathing that accompanies a hard effort." *(Jennifer Maculiewicz, Claremont, New Hampshire)*

"I love the results of running—my complexion is great, my body is down from a size eleven to size eight." *(Beverly Clark, Mountain View, California)*

"If things during the day aren't going well, I've got running to hang on to and a definite direction to follow." *(Wendy Bogerd, Escondido, California)*

This is just a cross-section of views held by women. There are certainly other good reasons not mentioned here that inspire women to start and keep running. Whether the reasons are physical, psychological, emotional or even spiritual, they all translate to an improved quality of life for the runner.

FOURTEEN: THE YOUNG WOMAN RUNNER

As in many American sports, running has its share of pushy parents who demand too much from their running children. In *Runner's World's* November 1983 issue, Kevin Baxter addressed this growing problem. He cited a successful age-group coach in Southern California who places so much pressure on his girls that they often *start* a race in tears. It would be easy to place immediate blame on the coach, but the true source of the problem lies elsewhere. That California coach continues to treat his young runners so harshly because they win. And for results like that, the parents put pressure on their daughters to stay with the regimented program.

Just like the fathers who scream at their sons on the baseball field, running is creating its own "Little League Syndrome," a term coined for overaggressive parents and coaches. Frank R. Collins, the TAC's national vice chairman, who supervises age-group cross country says, "The fathers push, push the kids. I'm against it. I don't think its good."

Because of Joan Benoit's recent Olympic marathon victory, some are predicting a boom in women's running in the United States. It is inevitable that some well-meaning parents will see the next Benoit in their seven- or eight-year-old daughter, urging her to start training seriously. Cases abound of talented, young runners who burn out early, losing interest in the sport before their potential can be given the chance to mature.

One young talent Baxter mentions is Tabitha Franks, a New Jersey girl who started running at the age of six. The parents were properly concerned and took their daughter to the Penn Sports Medicine Center to see if Tabitha could handle the stress running would place on her body. Initially, her parents tried to discourage her, to no avail. Tabitha's mother recalled, "The first few times Tabitha went running, I tried to get her to stop. I told her that running wasn't good for her and it was going to hurt her. I was a little apprehensive before her first marathon and my husband, who ran with her, said if at any time she felt bad, they'd stop right there. But she wanted to finish."

It is evident that the Franks have given their daughter plenty of opportunities to stop running. Her father explains that, "A lot of people have asked us whether we're afraid Tabitha will burn out. But we can't go up to her and say, 'Tabitha, don't run. You'll burn yourself out.' If we wait until she gets to high school, she might not be any good. At least she's had this success to enjoy." Indeed, Tabitha already owns several national records.

Was the Franks's concern for their daughter's health unfounded? Yes and no. Sportsmedicine authorities once were worried that running children could damage the soft, expanding growth plates at the joints. These plates or epiphyses do not fuse with the long bones until a child is in her late teens or early twenties. If the epiphyses are injured, the child's growth can be stunted. Although more and more children are donning running shoes, no significant increase has been reported in the number of growth-plate injuries.

Every child is different, though, and not all kids are built to withstand distance running. Dr. Robert Barnes, a leading sportsmedicine expert and authority on youth sports, claims, "There's no reason kids can't run distance. It's a very individual problem. Not every youngster can do it. But if the bones and joints will allow it, no problem."

Parents should not only be watchful of the stress that running is placing on their daughter's legs, but also the psychological impact competitive running could have on her. Baxter cites a study by the University of Oklahoma, in which young boys were divided into two groups at a summer camp. When the two groups were placed in competitive situations against one another, they developed much closer bonds to members within their group, and hostility to the opposing group. The experiment had to be halted when a few of the boys developed traces of serious psychological problems.

Parents who involve their daughters in running should then be aware of the overall experience the activity provides. Dr. Jack Wilmore, a member of the *Runner's World* Science Advisory Board, believes that youth sports should be designed to meet the needs of children, not parents. In *Athletic Training and Physical Fitness*, Dr. Wilmore states that "If the climate is such that winning is the only goal . . . the child will be likely to have a negative experience. If competition is organized . . . to satisfy the needs of the child and not the adult, the experience should be positive and facilitate sound emotional growth and psychological development." What Wilmore is telling parents is that their daughter should not run for Mom and Dad's ego or the 1996 Olympics, but rather, because she enjoys it as a playful activity.

To prevent the Little League Syndrome from claiming any more victims, Baxter included in his article *Runner's World's* advice for parents of running children and other adults who come in contact with young runners. *RW* suggests:

Each human being is created different, with individual strengths and individual flaws. Nowhere is this more evident than in running, where one runner's comfortable pace is another runner's PR. *Runner's World* appreciates this individuality, yet we believe that in the case of young runners, some guidelines must be established. To help keep our youngsters running through high school and beyond, *Runner's World* urges . . .

. . . no records be established or maintained for children younger than five. This pertains to *all* distances, not merely to the marathon.

. . . race directors to establish a minimum age limit of twelve for all races of marathon length or longer. In some European countries, runners younger than sixteen are not permitted to race at any distance greater than 3000 meters. While

that may be a bit drastic, the intentions of the rule are ap-
plauded. A youngster's bones and muscles don't develop
completely until the late teens or early twenties, and running
long distances before then is potentially harmful. A marathoner doesn't reach her prime until her late twenties, so
there's no need to do too much too soon.

. . . parents to hold their children out of competitive running events until the age of twelve. Running is a natural activity for children, but competitive road and track racing is
not. Competition places unnecessary pressure on children
and adults alike, but while adults are prepared to handle the
disappointment of losing, children aren't. "A lot of kids can't
handle defeat and are very poor sports about it," one age-
group coach says. The first objective of running should be
enjoyment. Competition can wait and, in fact, shouldn't be
stressed until a child is mature enough to handle it.

. . . young runners to make sure they have the proper
equipment. Developing bones and muscles are susceptible
to injury. The natural pounding and stress of running often
preys on this susceptibility, and without the proper shoes,
injury is almost certain. Comfortable, well-fitting socks can
prevent blisters, and loose, comfortable shorts can prevent
chafing.

Preventing young runners from being pushed by adults is
certainly a big problem. Yet perhaps even more troublesome
is the other group of children—those who don't exercise at
all. The general picture is quite bleak: Too many girls are
overweight and don't like to exercise. Dr. Mildred Cooper reported this finding in her book *Aerobics Training For Women*.
The research was conducted at a school in Jacksonville, Fla.,
with 502 participants. The participants ran for twelve minutes in the so-called "Cooper Test," and were classified according to the distance they completed:

324	very poor	(completed less than one mile)
148	poor	(completed between one and $1^{1}/_{8}$ miles)
28	average	(completed between $1^{1}/_{8}$ and $1^{1}/_{4}$ miles)

| 2 | good | (completed between $1^{1}/_{4}$ and $1^{2}/_{3}$ miles) |
| 0 | very good | (completed more than $1^{2}/_{3}$ miles) |

Dr. Cooper also established that the eight-year-old girls performed better overall than boys of the same age.

In San Antonio, Texas, in 1969, that same Cooper test was conducted with ninety-six girls who on the average were $14^{1}/_{2}$ years old, weighed 119 pounds and stood five-feet six-inches tall. Of the ninety-six untrained girls, only 26.1 percent ran more than $1^{1}/_{8}$ miles. After five weeks of training, these figures had reversed themselves: 64.8 percent ran more than $1^{1}/_{8}$ miles on that moderate training background.

Such a test shows that although young girls may on the whole be out of shape, it would not take much work to raise their level of fitness significantly.

Case Histories

There is a great variety in the type of running experience young girls have. When Annette Wild was seventeen years old, she was the only runner in her neighborhood and had to put up with a lot of criticism. At parties she was scorned for not smoking, and her running was looked upon as foolish. In stark contrast to Wild's unpleasant experience was that of Birgit Schillinger. As a seventeen-year-old, Schillinger found running to be a wonderful opportunity to appreciate the natural beauty of her environment. She was so inspired by her runs that she composed poetry based on her impressions of the outings.

Another woman who loved running was Manuela Angenvoorth-Preuss. Angenvoorth-Preuss began running at the age of fifteen and later developed into a world-class marathoner. She still runs today, if not as ambitiously. As a young woman, she always ran immediately after work, regardless of the weather. I had to talk her out of many races. If she had had her own way, she would have been running every weekend. Such enthusiasm among young women runners has its drawbacks. With more free time at their disposal than, say, a housewife, young girls with intense training programs like

Angenvoorth-Preuss could suffer from overtraining and chronic injuries. Hence, the most ambitious runners are often forced to take week-long rests to recover from injuries or fatigue.

Mary Decker is America's best-known and fastest middle-distance runner. Like Angenvoorth-Preuss, Decker had a penchant for overtraining as a youngster and has suffered numerous injuries during her running career. A world-class runner since she was a teenager, Decker has been training intensively for more than ten years. At the urging of a playmate, she entered her first race as an eleven-year-old. An age-group coach took Decker under his wing, and proceeded to overwork her. On a single weekend, he ran her in a marathon and two track races.

Despite such ill-advised racing, she improved steadily. With all of her immense talent, Decker has not been able to complete an Olympic final. Probably good enough to make the Olympic team when she thirteen years old, Decker was too young to run in Munich (a runner must be at least fourteen to compete internationally). In 1976 she couldn't compete in the Montreal Olympic Games because she was injured, and was kept out of the 1980 Games in Moscow because of the boycott. Bad luck followed her to the 1984 Games in Los Angeles, where a controversial midrace collision in the 3000 meters left her sprawled on the infield. The year before, Decker had claimed her first major international victory in the inaugural World Championships of Track and Field in Helsinki, where she won gold medals in both the 1500 and 3000 meters.

Even with that success, though, Decker remembers her childhood as providing her most memorable race. "There was one race I ran in when I was thirteen years old that I'll always remember," she says. "It was a race that was set up especially for me at UCLA so that I could break five minutes for a mile. There were officials, timers and my grandparents. Since I was thirteen, I wasn't allowed to run open races and I needed some competition to push me under five minutes. So Cyndy Poor, Kathy Gibbons and Judy Graham agreed to help me. So we ran the mile and I won in a brand new pair of shoes in 4:55. I'll always remember that race."

In summary, young girls are more predisposed to running than young boys, due to their favorable heart size/body weight ratio. Young women can reap the same general benefits that adult women gain from running: physical and emotional well-being. Since children often become overenthused with activities they enjoy, however, they are particularly susceptible to overtraining and subsequent burn-out, a condition in which they lose interest in the sport and give it up all together. Although there is no evidence available that running will cause long-term damage to young runners, parents should monitor their daughter's running to make sure her joints and bones will tolerate the stress. She should feel no pressure to run for any reason, and the activity should be a positive one for her, both physically and psychologically. The Cooper Test has shown that the fitness level of young, overweight girls can be dramatically improved with a minimal amount of training.

FIFTEEN: RUNNING UNTIL THE LAST DAY OF PREGNANCY

There are women who have run until the last day of their pregnancy and have delivered a healthy baby. There are other women who have achieved personal records in the marathon during their menstrual periods. Years ago that would have been inconceivable; the prejudices against remaining active during menstruation had piled so high, particularly in long distance running, that only a few courageous women gradually overcame these prejudices, most of them under medical supervision. This chapter, then, will discuss the following topics as they relate to the woman runner: hormonal changes, pregnancy, birth, and the lactation period.

A ten-year-old girl, lacking the curves that come with the onset of puberty, is as slim as a young boy. At this time she can run as well as a boy of the same age. Because of her favorable heart size/body weight ratio—as proven by Dr. van Aaken—this young girl has the potential to produce excellent endurance runs. Even if her parents train regularly, they must work hard and ambitiously to surpass the natural ability of their daughter. Thus, if parents want their children to start running, they should introduce them to the sport before puberty. Beginning after this period is more difficult, and if they want to start running again as adults after a long layoff, it will be easier if they ran as children. On the other hand, adults and coaches should not push a young runner too hard: Training and races should be low-key. This holds true for both young boys and girls.

Most girls reach puberty when they are eleven years old, although it may start as early as age nine or as late as age fourteen. As a result of the secretion of female hormones, the pelvis grows, the face becomes fuller, the breasts start to fill out and fatty deposits start to form on the hips. The sex organs become larger and pubic hair starts to grow. During this time the girl becomes physiologically ready for her first menstrual period.

Menstruation

This first menstruation is a shocking experience for many young girls, even if they are better educated about periods than their mothers were. Therefore, it is surprising to hear that girls today feel more insecure about secondary effects such as acne, sudden weight gain or heavy sweating than about the menstruation itself. Dr. Inge Bausenwein, a 1952 Olympic javelin thrower, published test results that showed that the performances of female athletes were not noticeably impaired during their menstrual periods. In some cases, these women posted their best times during menstruation. (They did, however, experience a drop-off in performance in the days leading up to menstruation.)

Prerace stress can often result in the period occurring earlier than usual. This is precisely what happened to Christa Vahlensieck at the Women's International Marathon in 1974, in West Germany. In spite of her prerace problems, Vahlensieck won over the best marathoners in the world that day, outkicking Kim Merritt of Chicago in the last mile and a half.

To avoid causing an unwanted early menstrual period, female competitors occasionally adopt the following method: They continue using birth control pills once per month (as prescribed), but take them over a longer period of time without a break. This procedure can be carried out either months before the event—resulting in a general alteration of the menstrual cycle—or just before the race in question. Such manipulation of the cycle is probably not harmful if done only once per year. You should avoid taking hormone pills, as their side effects are unpredictable.

Endurance and Pregnancy

The longest continuous human endurance activity takes place in the pregnant woman from the time of conception to the birth of her child. Yet if a woman runner is pregnant and discusses the subject of remaining active during the pregnancy with her doctor, he will usually relegate her to prenatal exercises. Dr. van Aaken was very experienced in these matters. He advised: "The woman who is used to running should continue running up until the expected delivery date of the baby. We have observed many cases of pregnant women continuing to run, and their deliveries were the easiest. There was one woman who ran until the very last day of pregnancy. After she ran four kilometers contractions started. She was able to reach the hospital, and within five minutes, gave birth to a healthy baby! Such women can begin floor exercises to strengthen the abdominal muscles and pelvis the very next day, and can thus retone the muscles in a very short period."

The sight of a pregnant woman running is no longer such a strange occurrence. Jackie Hansen, a former world-record holder in the marathon, ran a San Francisco 10-K in about one hour while in her eighth month of pregnancy. Her body had changed markedly. She was heavier and became short of breath easier, so she had to run slower than usual. Still, she had not lost her quick rate of recovery after the race.

A healthy woman runner does not face a higher risk of miscarriage than a nonrunning mother. On the contrary, the runner will notice a stabilizing of morning sickness, and she will be spared the typical excess weight gain. In addition, her back muscles will remain strong, providing her with an improved gait and also better preparing her for birth when the contractions start.

The pregnant woman, however, should avoid races and training at a fast pace after the first few months of pregnancy. It is also unwise to run on either rough or slippery surfaces, such as a rain-slickened or unpaved road. A pregnant woman should be particularly cautious about falling, because she is not only heavier, but also has a shifted center of gravity.

Dr. Patricia L. Hutchinson of the University of Georgia conducted a test with a thirty-two-year-old pregnant runner, gathering valuable information about the changes that a pregnant runner undergoes in her metabolism and circulation. From months three to eight the woman was tested on a treadmill, running the equivalent of a mile in ten minutes. The test showed that the woman's oxygen uptake increased in direct proportion to her body weight. Her respiratory and maximal pulse rate, however, increased by an even greater factor than the oxygen uptake. Hence, the woman's maximal pulse rate was 160 beats per minute in the third to fifth months, and rose to 175 in month eight. Four weeks after the birth, her maximal pulse rate had dropped again to 145 beats per minute. During the same period (months five to eight) her weight rose from 134 pounds to 138 pounds. In contrast, her maximal oxygen uptake hardly changed. Dr. Hutchinson concluded: "Running demands additional energy by placing gradually more stress on the system, as shown by the noticeable increase in the uptake of oxygen, as well as the pulse and respiratory rate. To place a constant work load on the body, the pregnant woman should gradually reduce her running pace as her expected delivery date approaches.

Running Through Pregnancy

The Finn Irja Paukkonen was a well-known marathoner in Finland with a best time of 2:52:33 when she became pregnant in 1977. Since people then were still very cautious about participating in endurance sports while pregnant, Paukkonen was left to her own devices. In her first month of pregnancy, October, she ran 160 miles. "In the beginning I was wary about running too much, but in November I upped my mileage to 225 and in December ran 185 miles," she explained. In January, her weight rose from 112 pounds to 121 pounds and she maintained her monthly total of 185 miles.

By February she had reduced her mileage to 100, yet added 120 to 200 miles of cross country skiing per month. She added, "In March I did 180 to 250 miles of skiing. I was less sure of running at this point in the pregnancy, since I had read somewhere that it could have damaging consequences."

At this point, she decided to accompany her husband on his training runs with a bicycle. "I often got stares from onlookers who were unaccustomed to the sight of a pregnant woman on a bicycle. I had never gotten a lot of pleasure from bicycling; my legs wanted to run. After reading about an American woman who had jogged the entire time she was pregnant, I was encouraged to start running again. At first, I dared run only one and a half miles, each time after bicycling. In the first week of May, then, I ran about six miles per week. The following week I ran two and a half miles at an eight-minute pace and felt fairly comfortable afterward. In my eighth month of pregnancy, I already weighed 132 pounds. In June I ran six to nine miles per week and swam occasionally. During this month I wanted to see how much of my speed I had retained, so I ran sixty yards in about eleven seconds . . ."

By July, she said, "The waiting became unbearable and I began to jog gently on a wooded trail, careful not to let myself be seen by anyone. They would have thought, 'That woman is crazy.' I covered the four miles at an eight-minute mile pace. On July fourth, I was admitted to the hospital, and I gave birth to a seven-pound boy the next day. It was a wonderful experience. My husband was present at the delivery—the most beautiful day of my life. While in the hospital I began to stretch and ran a few stairs early in the morning, so that no one could see me and think I was out of my mind."

On July 13, Irja Paukkonen ran 1.5 miles and bicycled 13.5 miles the next day. Two days later she tested her basic speed again and clocked 9.1 seconds for sixty yards and sixteen seconds for 100 yards. Initially, her legs hurt, but she persevered and continued to progress quickly. On August 4, she ran her first race after giving birth, one mile in 5:15. In the fall, she increased her training to thirty to forty-five miles per week. At the time, she was breast-feeding her baby, who was progressing well. Paukkonnen noted, "My breast milk held up despite my running. I would be pleased if expectant mothers could learn from my experience, particularly those who wanted to remain active during their pregnancy. Contact a sports doctor and you'll soon be on the roads running!"

Swiss runner Ursula Blunier had a completely different experience. She was a twenty-eight-year-old secretary, married and pregnant—though she wasn't aware of it—just as she started running. Hence, her body went through two different changes. After reading a book about running, she began running two miles every other day. She followed up each run with stretching, swimming and a sauna. After two months she participated in a 10-K and was disappointed with her fitness level. Blunier commented that, "Two weeks later, though, I successfully completed another 10-K and was encouraged. By the end of September, three months after I began running, my muscles had adjusted to the running, and I felt that this was the right activity for me." Then came the surprise: "I had a checkup with my gynecologist at the end of September, and I was concerned, because I knew that he would probably again prescribe injections since I had missed my period for the last six months. Yet my concerns were unfounded, as the doctor said that I was four months pregnant, and had not gained any weight yet nor had any difficulties."

Blunier was still unsure of herself, because of the dearth of literature on running while pregnant. In spite of advice to the contrary, she started her own training program. She believes: "I was fortunate that I did not know about the first few months of my pregnancy. If I had known, I would have worried unnecessarily. So I began my running care-free and was pleased with my slow but continuous improvement. I was feeling better than ever and learned to appreciate and cherish the weather, be it raining or cold. Within a short period of time, my running had fit into my daily routine, along with my hour of calisthenics, swimming and eight hours of secretarial work. I often painted on weekends, and my life was fulfilling. In no way did I feel I was overextending myself."

Blunier could scarcely believe it when she heard the news of her pregnancy. By the end of her fourth month, she could still fit into her clothes and she had gained very little weight. Her doctor advised her to stop competing in any sports. Her friends were also skeptical of her running while pregnant. Blunier continued, nonetheless. "I had monitored my body reactions more frequently and observed my overall condition and noticed quite quickly that running daily could only help me. For example, if I did not run one day, I felt noticeably more tired, weak and unwilling to take on tasks. An-

other advantage of my training was that during my pregnancy I was able to give in to the eating binges most women experience, without the accompanying weight gain."

Mrs. Blunier's doctor urged her to at least curb her mileage, advice she ignored. She was too pleased with her minimal weight gain of eight pounds after six months and only eleven pounds at the end of her pregnancy. "Running became difficult from the end of the sixth month to the end of the seventh month, for my increased weight was now making breathing difficult when I ran hills. In addition, my body was becoming more round and losing its tone. However, I did not give up and was all the more pleased when the fetus shifted down into the lower part of the abdomen, allowing me to breathe easy once again.

"Besides the typical problem of tiring more easily, I still had no difficulties up until the day I gave birth. On the day I delivered my daughter, I ran five miles on a sunny winter day. Afterwards, I felt physically tired but also refreshed and recovered."

The delivery was completed within two hours, and Mrs. Blunier's daughter was healthy and cheerful. Four days after giving birth, she had resumed her normal weight. She started running again after twelve days. Two months later she was running thirty-five to forty-five miles per week. Says Blunier: "I am satisfied and happy with my new position as mother and housewife. I attribute a great deal of this well-being to running."

Here, then, is the training schedule of Ursula Blunier during her pregnancy:

Month 1:	7 miles per week
Month 2:	13 miles per week
Month 3:	20 to 25 miles per week
Month 4:	30 miles per week
Month 5:	30 miles per week
Month 6:	30 miles per week
Month 7:	25 miles per week
Month 8:	40 miles per week
Month 9:	30 miles per week (five miles on the day of delivery!)

Dorothy Federhen found herself in another situation all together. She had already had three children, and was running for the third year when she became pregnant again. She had been encouraged by the articles in *Spiridon* magazine stating that it was possible to continue running while pregnant. Her fourth pregnancy was her easiest, one in which she ran up to the day before the delivery.

Federhen was five-feet three-inches tall and normally weighed 101 pounds. In her thirty-second week she weighed 110 pounds, and her maximum weight during pregnancy was 122 pounds. She gave birth to a seven and a half pound boy, whom she breast-fed while resuming training. Shortly after the delivery, she had lost all of her excess weight.

She describes her training before the pregnancy: "I ran about thirty miles per week, making sure to run at least thirty minutes every day; I really couldn't spare much more time away from my housework. I preferred running on an empty stomach in the morning, before breakfast. This early running was my best protection during the length of the pregnancy. My early runs provided two benefits: First, when I ran on an empty stomach, I ran unencumbered with food, and second, at that time of day I missed most of the gawkers. During the first trimester my mileage did not change, because I didn't gain weight. The nausea and morning sickness that accompany pregnancy diminished with my morning runs. After a few minutes of running, both conditions disappeared all together. What a difference from my three previous pregnancies!"

She did stop running on the track and participating in races. Federhen explains: "I ran regularly, yet always according to how well I felt. When necessary, I walked. From about the fifteenth week on, I suffered pains from varicose veins in the hip area, which had proved troublesome in my third pregnancy as well. I took medicine for the first case, though it was not necessary the second time around. My morning runs reduced the pain of the varicose veins considerably, although they were as pronounced as during the third pregnancy.

"As I gained weight, my training pace slowed. I can now understand how an overweight runner must feel. From an initial pace of eight minutes per mile, my tempo dropped off to ten minutes per mile up to week thirty-five. After the fetus dropped to a lower position in my abdomen, I was able to regain some of my initial pace. Again, I was able to run one and a half to two miles without requiring a walking break.

"Comparing my fourth pregnancy with the previous three, I did not suffer from shortness of breath during my last term. Even in extreme weather conditions I did not experience any circulatory problems, as evidenced by my steady blood pressure of 100 over 50. My varicose veins did not worsen. In general, the runs improved my daily functioning: I slept well, completed housework and took care of the family adequately, was in good spirits most of the time, staved off illnesses, and learned to appreciate the invigorating feeling of getting up early. Running also kept my back muscles toned and aligned, preventing my gait from deteriorating, as is often the case with pregnant women.

"If you view birth as a physical activity requiring maximum exertion, then daily exercise such as running becomes imperative. The energy you expend in preparation pays off handsomely when you go into labor. In addition to running, I also did daily gymnastics and relaxation exercises. The day before the delivery, I ran two and a half miles on the track. This daily regimen made the labor pains themselves easier to endure. When the amniotic sac burst, I was put to bed and after forty-five minutes of contractions, my son was born— without pain-killers or other medicine. The oxygen deficit I incurred during the contractions was offset by the sufficient pauses between contractions. The labor was indeed difficult, but at no times did I feel incapacitated. I hope that all women who run through their pregnancy will come through their labor as well as I did."

When Federhen was released from the hospital after one week, she ran twice daily for five minutes in her apartment. Four weeks later she resumed normal training.

She stated: "I simultaneously breast-fed my third child and began running because I was plagued by severe circulatory problems. Running was my alternative to the doctor's orders that I take medicine to stave off the circulation problems and stop lactating. I thought that the running itself would help me to stop lactating. But I was far off the mark! Instead, the stimulation and subsequent stabilizing of the circulation led to an increase in milk production, more in fact than my son required. I was able to nurse my son for another eight months, until he actually refused my milk."

Federhen gives women runners the following tips: "If you run at the end of the lactation period, run after nursing if your baby has nursed from both breasts. Be sure to wear a good-fitting bra when running; a normal nursing bra is inadequate."

Dr. Hegall Vollert, a runner, presents our last example. Dr. Vollert's wife gave birth at the end of 1981. He stated: "My wife had been running for four years when she became pregnant, and she continued to train after the pregnancy. Granted, many doubters made her unsure about the decision, but I was able to assuage her concerns rather easily. Her decision to continue was made easier by the simple fact that she enjoyed running so much. After becoming pregnant, her pace slowed markedly in the very first month because of the hormonal adjustment. What I found even more amazing was that only a few days before the delivery, she ran with no more difficulty, although she had gained an unusual amount of weight, about forty pounds (from 103 to 143 pounds). The training consisted of two and a half to four miles of running, five times per week.

"In all of my days of practice, I have never seen such a well-balanced pregnant woman, both emotionally and physically. She never suffered bouts of depression, vomiting or pain. At no time during the pregnancy did I have to worry about her health. When she was in her eighth month, we went to northern Spain for vacation. She was as fit as before the pregnancy. Her endurance, both in and out of the water, demonstrated to the other women the true meaning of being healthy.

"The pre-birth period was unusually long because of the fetus's unfavorable positioning. Normally this problem requires a Caesarean, a procedure my wife refused. Her endurance and strong stomach muscles allowed her to forgo the surgery. The child is noticeably active and healthy, weighing almost eight pounds at birth. Fourteen days later my wife began running and had already returned to her normal weight of 103 pounds."

When Menstruation Doesn't Occur

Despite cases such as that of Dr. Vollert's wife, misconceptions persist. Newspapers present the story somewhat differently, printing headlines such as "Running Causes Infertility" and "Jogging Works as a Contraceptive." Both ideas are, of course, nonsense, yet such articles trouble women runners and women thinking of taking up the sport.

The example of beginning runner Ursula Blunier described earlier is a strong argument against such accusations. Perhaps even more convincing evidence is the story of Miki Gorman, a world-class masters runner. Exactly nine months after running the New York Marathon in 2:39:11 (then an American record), she became a first-time mother at the age of forty-one. Running interfered with neither the conception nor the actual pregnancy.

An expert in the subject is Mona M. Shangold, M.D., a runner for eighteen years, and women's editor for *Runner's World* magazine. For two years she analyzed questionnaires handed out to the women participants of the New York City Marathon. The survey revealed that 24 percent of the marathoners had menstrual problems or cessation of menstruation all together (amenorrhea), compared to five percent for the general population. It must be noted, however, that 20 percent of those runners suffered from this problem before they started running. According to Shangold, the woman marathoner is highly motivated and exposes herself to stressful situations and lives and works in a goal-oriented fashion. This type of person is particularly vulnerable to hormonal disturbances, whether she runs or not. Also susceptible are women who lose a lot of body weight or body fat, or are naturally of a slight build. All changes in the metabolism of fat can effect the estrogen level, resulting in less serious menstrual problems.

"When you consider the extraordinary coordination required for the hormonal processes, it is more surprising that women ovulate and menstruate regularly than it is that they occasionally have hormonal problems," Shangold continues. She means that we shouldn't take the problems too seriously: "In most cases, women who regularly have their period continue to have regular periods when they become athletes." In any case, if you ever miss a period, you should consult a gynecologist.

Since women's long-distance running is still a relatively young sport, and many of the women surveyed by Shangold were probably in their first year of intensive marathon training, data obtained from military schools is also germane to our discussion. In the United States, women recruits must do the same training routines as their male counterparts. Studies of these women have revealed that 85 percent experienced menstrual problems at the beginning of training, compared to only 15 percent after the two years of training. Based on the results of this study, we can assume that those women beginning to train for marathons are like the new recruits: Over time they will also have noticeably fewer menstrual problems.

A large number of women report that after taking up running, their menstrual bleeding is less pronounced, either in the quantity of blood expelled or in the severity of the abdominal cramping.

A lengthy discussion of the various birth control devices does not fall within the scope of this book. It's noteworthy to mention, though, that most women prefer the barrier method of birth control, the most common devices being diaphragms or vaginal sponges. Neither device has any long-term side effects. The diaphragm's only drawback is that women must accustom themselves to inserting it, a process that some couples feel disrupts intercourse. The sponge's main drawback is its price; at $1 per sponge, it may be costly to couples who have sex often.

Some women refuse to try birth control pills because they don't want to ingest chemicals unnecessarily. According to Michael Policar, M.D., the medical director of San Francisco's Planned Parenthood, women who take birth control pills don't face a higher risk of cancer than women who use other methods. Many women who were on the pill have decided to discontinue taking it because of its bothersome side effects: breakthrough bleeding (bleeding at irregular periods of the menstrual cycle), weight gain and water retention, breast swelling and mood changes (especially depression).

Another alternative is the intrauterine device (IUD), but the insertion of this device can cause minor bleeding and cramps, as well as infections. A greater incidence of pelvic inflammatory disease occurs in women who use the IUD. Since this disease has been known to cause sterility, the IUD should be avoided by women who wish to bear children. Women should consult their doctors to determine which method of birth control best meets their needs.

The Hormones of Women

A final discussion on the basic hormone processes is taken up by Dr. Wolfgang Klemm of East Germany: When speaking of women's hormones, we should narrow the topic to a discussion of the sex hormones. These hormones consist of three groups, which are produced in both the ovaries and the adrenal cortex. During pregnancy, a third area of production is the placenta.

The estrogens. The most important representative of this group is estradiol, named for its ability to induce estrus among lower mammals. These hormones are responsible for the growth of the primary and secondary sex organs and for the shaping of the female body. They also effect the growth of long bones and stimulate cell metabolism of the estrogen-sensitive tissues. In the menstrual cycle, they terminate the menstrual bleeding and control the first main phase of the cycle (proliferation) leading up to ovulation. The woman feels relaxed, balanced, refreshed and resilient. Her recovery rate will be high in the one to two weeks after menstruation.

The gestagens (corpus luteum hormones). The most important representative of this group is progesterone. The gestagens are produced during and after ovulation and control the second main phase of the cycle (secretion). These hormones function to both support and control the effect of the estrogens; gestagens act as a kind of counterforce to the estrogen and thus maintain hormonal equilibrium in the body. When ovulation occurs, the body's nervous system reaches a state of ergotrophy, when the body has a greater tendency to expend energy than to store it. In this state, women can produce short, intensive workouts during this part of the monthly cycle. At the same time, however, a woman's reactions are hurried, exaggerated and uneconomical, so that the energy reserves accumulated in the estrogen phase are soon depleted. Muscle cramps (especially abdominal) are common toward the end of this phase, which can easily worsen a woman's overall condition. Efficient endurance efforts are seldom achieved in this phase.

The androgens (male sex hormones). The most important representative of this group is testosterone. Androgens are also present in women's bodies, although in quantities ten to thirteen times less than in men. In women their function is to encourage the development of the secondary sex characteristics, especially to produce body hair, form the musculature and protect the sexual functions. After ovulation, the production of these hormones increases suddenly for two days, after which time the hormone level drops off, yet remains higher than in the first half of the menstrual cycle. In addition to the regulating of the sexual functions, androgens raise the overall activity level of the body and hence belong to the second half of the menstrual cycle.

Chemically, androgens are related to the gestagens. Although these hormones have been synthetically produced, the synthetic hormones' effects will actually encompass the effects of both androgens and gestagens. When taking the pill, the menstrual cycle is disrupted. The overall functioning of the hormones, then, is determined by the birth control pill itself, be it influenced by estrogen, gestagen or (rarely) a balance of the two. Therefore, the reactions to the pill vary greatly among individuals, and it should be taken only under the supervision of your gynecologist.

When these three hormone groups exist in balanced quantities in the woman, she is classified as a *balanced type*. However, such a balance among the hormones rarely exists. Usually one or the other hormones will exert more influence.

The estrogen-type. In this body type, all of the body parts are especially rounded by the presence of fatty deposits, which result over time in a stocky build. The psychological profile of such a woman is usually calm, passive and with slow reactions. These women are rarely interested in sports.

The gestagen-type. Because of a relatively low level of estrogen in the body, this woman is usually slim, very active and has fast reactions. This kind of woman is well-suited for sports. Her increased endurance is caused by her fewer fat deposits. On the other hand, her recovery rate is slower as a result.

The androgen-type. This body type is influenced by an increased production of the hormone androgen. Hence, the body has a strong skeletal structure and larger muscle mass. The face is more striking in appearance. Women of this type are usually serious, practical and down-to-earth. They also demonstrate a strong interest in sports. Although they do not achieve as much in endurance sports as gestagen-type women, they do show an aptitude for such activities.

Sports Gynecology

Sports gynecology is an innovative development on the women's running scene. Born from a direct need to examine the effects of exercise and running on the female reproductive system, sports gynecology is destroying many of the myths perpetuated by too little information.

One of the most important factors in a healthy woman's physiological chemistry is a consistent menstrual cycle and one of the most talked about topics within sports gynecology is menstrual irregularity in athletes. Many women runners experience irregular periods, and some stop having periods all together. In the non-athletic world, many women experience the same problems. Obviously, any woman with either of these problems should consult her gynecologist.

There are some general guidelines, however, that you can follow: Menstruating every twenty-five to thirty-two days is probably perfectly normal. Menstruating every twenty to sixty days is also quite acceptable as long as the woman is not trying to become pregnant; but a woman whose periods occur more frequently than every twenty days and less often than sixty days, or bleeds between periods, or notices a discharge from one or both breasts, should consult her physician immediately. Do not listen to friends who make light of these symptoms—they could lead to serious health problems. Because women's running has only developed (in a major way) rather recently, we do not know the long-term effects running has on our bodies. There is little evidence that running is harmful, but much evidence that it is beneficial.

Toxic Shock Syndrome

Another topic of paramount importance to the female runner is toxic shock syndrome. Even though reported cases of this disease are still rare, there still are facts that must be looked at closely, and every woman should keep up with what information is available.

Women runners obviously prefer tampons to sanitary napkins because of the freedom it allows them when they move, the lack of messiness and the comfort (as opposed to a soggy, shifting pad). Current information on toxic shock syndrome confirms that the woman runner can still use tampons, but she must be aware of certain signals that warrant suspicion. Here are some recognizable symptoms during menstruation: vomiting, diarrhea, muscle aches, sore throat and fever. Should any of these symptoms appear while you are wearing a tampon, remove it immediately and call your physician. One way of dealing with worry about toxic shock syndrome is to wear a sanitary napkin intermittently in place of a tampon—or, of course, you can choose to stop wearing a tampon all together. But the probability of the bacterial infection invading your body is so small that most physicians still consider tampons safe.

What about the effect of running on women's breasts? The general consensus is that women with small breasts enjoy braless running and women whose breasts are large enough to bounce prefer to wear bras with good built-in support. Small-breasted women may experience nipple irritation during their runs. One way of dealing with this problem is to place an adhesive bandage over the nipple. Most women experience tenderness in their breasts during menstruation— wearing a bra while running helps reduce this pain.

SIXTEEN:
LIFE BEGINS
AT 40

Dr. Paul Dudley White, President Dwight Eisenhower's physician, once stated, "The greatest challenge of public and private health today, and the most neglected, is that of physical fitness in middle age. It transcends, I believe, the problems of health of both youth and senility." As White explained, young people should certainly exercise, but more importantly, they should maintain a healthy lifestyle into middle age. Many Americans do not.

What can be gained by staying active through the middle years of life? Exercise performs three vital functions:

1) *Exercise stimulates circulation.* Your circulation increases when you work your muscles. The oxygen demand of the muscles increases, and to satisfy this demand, the heart beats stronger. As your cells receive oxygen, you'll feel better. In addition, when the heart pumps more blood to these active muscle groups, they become more efficient.

2) *Exercise builds endurance.* A healthy person can perform a given activity more efficiently than an unfit person. She can maintain this effort over a longer period of time.

3) *Exercise helps you relax.* A good workout will do wonders for stress and tension. One of the best ways to relax is to do some kind of exercise, because muscle fatigue leads naturally to physical and mental rest.

The Aging Process

Around age twenty-six, our body systems begin to decline, a process that takes about fifty years. How does this decline affect athletic performance? In most sports, athletes reach their physical peaks in their late twenties, although variation is great. Swimmers are considered over-the-hill by age twenty-four and gymnasts lose their competitive edge by their late teens.

Until recently, long-distance runners were thought to peak around twenty-eight or twenty-nine. But when Portugal's Carlos Lopes won the 1984 Olympic marathon at the age of thirty-seven, it forced people to reconsider. Lopes has been a world-class athlete for many years (10,000-meter silver medalist in the '76 Olympics), and has maintained this level of fitness up to the present time remarkably well. He prefaced his marathon victory in Los Angeles with an extraordinary 27:17 in the 10,000 meters, breaking the former world record (although he finished second to countryman Fernando Mamede).

Middle-aged women, meanwhile, can look to forty-seven-year-old Joyce Smith of Great Britain for inspiration. Like Lopes, Smith has been a world-class athlete for many years, with a marathon PR of 2:29. At the Olympic marathon in Los Angeles, she ran an extraordinary 2:34, very close to her all-time best. Although the average middle-aged runner is less interested in fast times than simply maintaining fitness, Smith's career shows that the human body can be pushed much farther for a longer time than people thought possible.

Although not quite in Smith's class, Sister Marion Irvine is another extra-ordinary middle-aged runner. She is a 54-year-old Catholic nun and principal at Sacred Heart School in San Francisco. She became the oldest qualifier for the 1984 Olympic Trials by running 2:51:01 at the California International Marathon. She also produced six national age-group records, including a 37:43 10-K, 1:02:58 for 10 miles and a 1:23:16 half-marathon. Sister Marion runs between seventy and eighty miles per week, fitting in her running around her school work. She's up before six to say prayers with the other convent sisters, then completes her daily run before returning to Sacred Heart.

Thomas Bassler, a Los Angeles-area physician, states, "Our concepts of aging and athletics are going to change. We may find out that the peak performance may be around twenty-nine, but the slope afterward is not as steep as we think it may be." Although many people run because they enjoy the activity itself, the sport offers undeniable health benefits as well.

Kenneth H. Cooper, M.D., states flatly, "You definitely get more benefit—and more quickly—from running than any other exercise." The greatest benefits are in the cardiovascular system. Dr. David L. Costill of the Human Performance Laboratory at Ball State University specifies those benefits: "In order to metabolize excessive fats from your blood stream, you need to do your exercise at relatively low intensity and for a long period of time." As Costill maintains, running is among the very best exercises to accomplish that task.

Cholesterol is a fatty alcohol that has been linked to coronary disease. It is not only found in all animal fats, egg yolks, meat and shellfish, but is also produced by our body. If you consume too much cholesterol, it will build up, most notably in your arteries in the form of plaque. Although it is not yet completely understood how the high level of cholesterol in the blood leads to this plaque buildup, doctors agree that it can clog the arteries, restricting blood flow and make the person more vulnerable to heart attacks.

This clogging of the arteries can take years to develop. By eating foods high in cholesterol and not maintaining an active lifestyle in her twenties and thirties, a middle-aged woman (and a man to an even greater extent) can face an early coronary disease or heart attack. Costill believes that middle-aged persons are most vulnerable to cardiovascular problems due to oxygen deficiency (restricted blood flow from clogged arteries results in less oxygen being transported to the vital organs). He states, "The critical years in terms of cardiovascular disease are between twenty-five and thirty-five. That's the era of a man's life, and a woman's too, when they will pay the least attention to their physical health . . . Once you build up atherosclerotic deposits in your system, you rarely get rid of them . . . even by exercise. At best, you can stop the build-up of more deposits, or hope that by

Sister Marion Irvine, a school principal, has set six national age-group records.

being better trained you will have more strength to survive a heart attack, should it occur."

Starting out

After reading Costill's words of warning, the out-of-shape, middle-aged woman might start jogging immediately or enroll in an aerobics class. To take up exercise after years of neglect might be the worst thing you could do. Any book on exercise should include the following warning: *Do not start any vigorous exercise without first consulting your physician.* Cooper adds another requirement: You should also get a stress test. Stories abound of people (usually men) dying of a heart attack after becoming active again. Nowadays, however, women are exhibiting an increased incidence of heart attacks. Although the exact causes of this relatively new health problem are not completely understood, stress, poor diet and lack of exercise certainly play contributing roles.

Both the American Heart Association and the American Running and Fitness Association recommend that all sedentary adults take a treadmill test before embarking on an exercise program.

To begin the test, the patient starts walking on a level treadmill while a physician monitors her EKG, blood pressure, pulse, appearance and symptoms. The treadmill is adjusted every three minutes to increase the rate and steepness of the grade. A fit person might be extended to run for fifteen minutes on a difficult 20 percent grade. EKG reports are printed out and analyzed every few minutes. Emergency medical supplies are in the testing room. After the test, the doctor analyzes the results, discusses them with the patient, and then outlines a sensible exercise program for her.

This test costs $150 to $300, depending on where you take it. If your test is done for important medical reasons (for example, you suspect there may be heart problems due to your family history), your health insurance may cover the expenses. Considering the potentially lethal danger of running with blocked arteries, the investment seems sound.

Racing in Middle Age

Middle-aged runners have certain advantages over younger athletes. They have a wealth of experience and knowledge accumulated through the years that can be applied to making a training program work. Unlike the sometimes impetuous younger runner, they understand the importance of moderation, especially as it applies to physical exercise.

Before racing, women should have at least one year of jogging background, preferably two, or an equivalent amount of bicycling, swimming or cross country skiing. By starting with this solid training background, you are likely to improve more steadily and avoid injuries.

Training, then, should be based on LSD, or long slow distance. Either you will have a training partner who also believes in LSD, or you must accept running many workouts by yourself. An important point to remember is to *never* race during workouts. Middle-aged runners often train with younger and faster partners, making this temptation all too easy. Such stressful workouts can lead to injury; most older runners are not injured during races but during hard workouts.

You should start each run carefully, after purposeful stretching. Just as you must gradually build up to longer, harder runs, though, you should gradually increase the extension and range of your stretches. People who run in the morning are particularly susceptible to injury, as the leg muscles have not yet been warmed and stretched by the day's activities. Middle-aged runners may even want to loosen up by riding a bike before running. Taking a short walk before the run would serve the same purpose.

Training For the Race

For the first six months of the training program, we recommend running five days per week, using the weekends for the weekly longer run. This longer run may only be eight miles initially, but with time, you will build up to runs of ten and twelve miles, with no greater effort than the shorter runs. All runs can be interrupted by intermittent stretching and drinking. It is important not only to drink enough fluids, but also to dress well. Better to wear too much than too little: If you bring too many layers, you can always take them off.

With diligence and care, you will complete the first six months relatively injury-free. For the next six months, your mileage should be increased, along with a slightly faster training pace. Set a goal for yourself: If you'd like to run a

10-K at a certain speed, your body will have to learn to run at that pace. Warm up well, and try to run one mile at the pace you want to maintain in the 10-K. Slow down to your normal pace for the next mile, and then alternate race pace and normal pace for the remaining miles of the workout. During the faster miles, take care to accelerate gradually; you shouldn't be finishing with a sprint. Try to hit top speed about halfway or two-thirds through the run. If the effort is forced, and you start having breathing problems or feel nauseated, back off to a slower pace.

On the roads it is easy to practice accelerating. You needn't depend on precise mile-markers; increasing your tempo between two trees would have the same effect. Over time, you'll cover the same distances more quickly and with less effort.

Many top runners follow the hard-easy pattern of training, always following up a hard workout with an easier one. This pattern allows the body to rest for the next hard run. You should also adopt this pattern in your program. You can run these faster workouts back-to-back only if you show restraint. If pain develops, slow down or stop.

Your First Race

When the first year of the program has been completed, you should seek out a local 10-K race or even a shorter fun-run. Look upon the race as part of your training. Be observant of other runners: How are they preparing for the race? Are they stretching? How much and what kind of stretches? What are they wearing? Are they drinking water or some kind of electrolyte solution? Find out what they ate for breakfast. Runners (especially older ones) are usually more than willing to share their preparation methods.

Another part of the learning process is to start the race with a training companion. You shouldn't feel obligated to match your companion's pace the entire race, but your friend may provide some helpful hints on how to start a race. Inexperienced racers typically start too quickly, caught up in the prerace excitement.

It is important to complete this first race. You've carefully followed a training program that was designed to prepare you for racing. If you feel uncomfortable during the race, slow down or try walking for a while. Do not continue, though, if you feel you're aggravating a condition that could lead to an injury.